RANSOMES OF IPSWICH

Portrait of Robert Ransome, Snr., born 1753, died 1830 (SP4/165)

UNIVERSITY OF READING

RANSOMES OF IPSWICH

A History of the Firm and Guide to its Records

by D. R. Grace and D. C. Phillips

Institute of Agricultural History
1975

Published by the Institute of Agricultural History,
University of Reading, Whiteknights, Reading, RG6 2AG

© University of Reading, 1975

ISBN: 0 7049 0144 7

Printed by
Unwin Brothers Limited
The Gresham Press
Old Woking Surrey England
A member of the Staples Printing Group

Contents

List of Plates

Acknowledgements

This publication arises out of the decision, taken in 1967, by the Institute's Museum of English Rural Life, to form a research collection of the historical records of the agricultural servicing and processing industries. The importance of this collection was recognised by the Social Science Research Council which since 1970 has underwritten the very considerable cost of its systematic documentation and detailed indexing. The records of Ransomes, Sims & Jefferies Ltd., form the single most important archive and we are heavily indebted to the firm for making its records available for research, for its enthusiastic support and not least generous financial assistance towards the publication of this book. The authors wish to thank all those members of the Institute Staff who have assisted them in many ways, in particular, Dr. E. J. T. Collins for his general direction and encouragement, Mrs. Raine Morgan for preparing the bibliography, and Mrs. P. Basten for typing and checking successive drafts of a difficult manuscript.

D. R. G.

D. C. P.

Institute of Agricultural History
University of Reading
October 1974

PART ONE

History of the Firm

RANSOMES OF IPSWICH:
A SHORT HISTORY

Early Years c. 1780–1835

Eighteenth century agricultural improvement was associated mainly with enclosure, reclamation and new rotational practices. Mechanisation, on the other hand, appeared only late on in the Agricultural Revolution and in many areas of Britain, especially the South and East, had no significant impact until the third quarter of the nineteenth century. While the majority of agricultural engineering firms came into existence after 1830, a few can trace their origins back to an earlier period, and Ransomes of Ipswich is one of these.

Robert Ransome, founder of the firm, was born in 1753, the son of a Quaker schoolmaster, at Wells in Norfolk.[1] Following apprenticeship to a Norwich ironmonger he went into business on his own, in the same city, setting up one of the first brass and iron foundries in East Anglia. His Quaker background may have helped him acquire an early reputation for good, reliable workmanship and it certainly seems to have been a benefit in that much of his initial financial support came from Mr. Gurney, a Quaker banker.[2] Quite naturally, considering his location, Ransome (trading fictitiously as "Ransome and Co.") found a great deal of his trade with farmers, primarily in the supply of plough shares. In 1785 he patented a method of tempering cast iron shares,[3] the first of a number of developments in this field. Even at this early stage he was more than just a local craftsman serving the immediate neighbourhood and advertisements show that Ransome's plough shares were marketed through some fifty agencies throughout Norfolk and Suffolk.[4]

In 1789 with a capital of £200 and one workman, the business was transferred to the thriving port of Ipswich which afforded readier access to markets and raw materials.[5] At his new foundry Ransome made the technological breakthrough which probably ensured his pre-eminence in plough manufacture. His "chilling" process, reputedly discovered by accident, produced a cast-iron share with a hard under-surface and a comparatively soft upper surface which kept itself sharp by the normal wear incurred in usage.[6] This single advance represented a giant step forward in plough technology, especially in respect of the light, dry soils, where wear and tear was substantial, and where much of the progress of the "agricultural revolution" was taking place. It also did a great deal to make the cast-iron share a more practical proposition as against the more laboriously manufactured wrought-iron share. Ransome soon earned a national reputation for his products, which were noticed and commended by the influential William Marshall, and which won him a number of awards at the early meetings of the Bath and West of England Agricultural Society.[7]

In 1808 he took out a third patent, this time for the manufacture of interchangeable plough parts, thus permitting rudimentary standardisation of plough bodies and the easier replacement of worn parts in the field.[8] The greater significance was that a large manufacturer was now able to produce a wide variety of local designs of plough by the interchange of detachable parts. Hitherto a barrier to large scale plough production had been the bewildering variety of local types and preferences which effectively prevented any one maker from capturing more than a small share of the market. Robert Ransome surmounted this problem not by breaking down local prejudices, but by adapting his products to conform to them.

Conditions were certainly favourable to the establishment of a thriving implement business at the turn of the century, when, during the Napoleonic Wars, the arable acreage was rapidly expanding. This first phase saw the emergence of a number of firms such as, Garretts of Leiston (1778), Hornsbys of Grantham (1815), Howards of Bedford (1811) and Bentalls of Maldon (1805), which were to be the backbone of the industry. Labour shortages encouraged early attempts at mechanisation, notably thrashing machines, but much of this work was done by itinerant millwrights who enjoyed only a short-lived reputation. The early agricultural engineers benefited more from the rising demand for traditional implements than from labour-saving machinery. Robert Ransome, in common with many of his contemporaries, restricted himself largely to plough manufacture and jobbing metal work. There is in fact no certainty as to the exact date at which he expanded his production from foundry work into the manufacture of complete ploughs, although he was making them by 1809.[9] Some suggestions have been made that he produced thrashing machines from 1800 onwards but this cannot be substantiated. Nevertheless, making the most of the wartime boom and also the special advantages created by East Anglia's dominant position in arable farming, Ransome made rapid strides. Surviving accounts show receipts almost doubling between 1809 and 1815,[10] at the time when the founder's son, James, having given up his own business in Yarmouth, joined his father at Ipswich.

Launched on the tide of a buoyant agriculture, Ransome and Son might have foundered with the onset of the agricultural depression which set in after 1815, following the collapse of the wartime boom. In some areas the arable acreage contracted while in many others a glutted labour market positively discouraged the adoption of labour-saving techniques. Had the firm been entirely dependent on agriculture it might have disappeared without trace, as did many other small concerns, or it may have been reduced to the status of a local foundry. Instead, however, the worst effects of depression were offset by non-agricultural work. In 1812 William Cubbitt, the famous civil engineer had entered into a contract as the firm's engineer and under his direction the scope of the business was expanded to take in bridge-building and mill-wrighting.[11] Cubbitt's role at this difficult time may have been crucial. A surviving account reveals that in his first four years at Ipswich, work valued at nearly £5,000 was gained which, it was claimed "would probably not have been undertaken without him".[12] In 1818 he supervised the construction of Stoke Bridge over the River Gipping. In 1819, again under Cubbitt's direction, Ransomes began the work to provide Ipswich with its gas supply, a contract which in that year accounted for almost 20 per cent of the firm's income.[13] The more stable civil engineering element did much to underpin Ransomes' more traditional work while agriculture was at a low ebb and enabled the firm to provide employment for 50–60 men and boys in the early 1820's.[14]

Cubbitt left in 1826 but retained informal contacts with the firm which included some co-operation in early railway work, and civil engineering remained important. The agricultural side of the business received a boost when James Allen Ransome, grandson of the founder, became a partner in 1830. His specialised technical appreciation of the problems of agricultural engineering, revealed in his successful book, *The Implements of Agriculture* (1843)—the best treatise on implements and machinery before the age of steam—probably led to an increase in the range and quality of farm products but the unfortunate lack of evidence relating to this period permits only conjecture. It would seem, however, that the demand for many classes of equipment, such as cultivators, land rollers and some types of thrashing machine reached significant proportions only in the late 1830's, which suggests that this was a vitally important time in the development of the industry. Prior to this we can only assume that business was kept ticking over by the plough trade and in particular by the fluctuating demand for plough shares.[15] The condition of agriculture between 1815 and 1835 was certainly not stable enough to encourage investment in elaborate machinery and there was a good deal of suspicion of labour saving devices as indicated by the hostility to thrashing machinery in the Swing Riots of 1830.

The Take-off: c. 1835–1850

The role of non-agricultural work is an interesting feature of the whole history of Ransomes, but of more than usual importance in this period, even though it is always dangerous to attribute too much to individuals in a business history, was the impact of Charles May, a fellow Quaker, who joined the firm in 1836. In many ways filling the vacuum left by Cubbitt, May was largely responsible for work arising from the railway building boom which was then gathering momentum. For a quarter of a century the firm was as well known for its railway parts as for its agricultural implements and it is arguable that for a good part of this period railway work was the real money-spinner. Most of the railway records were probably transferred to Ransomes & Rapier in 1869, and subsequently lost or destroyed, but a fair indication of its importance is revealed by the balance sheet for 1851 which shows agricultural work valued at £35,000 for the year as against nearly £87,000 for railway and general engineering work.[16] One or two sundry survivals show that a considerable amount of the trade was with the great railway building contractors, such as Peto and Betts and Thomas Brassey (the latter, in 1847, is known to have contracted for 2,400 wagons on one single occasion).[17] Contemporary evidence from other sources implies that Ransomes and May were best known for their chairs and fastenings (used in rail laying), for which a patent was taken out in 1841, and for chilled iron crossings which were an application of Robert Ransome's original method for plough shares.[18] Between 1847 and 1867 some 12,000 miles of railway at home and abroad were constructed using Ransomes' materials as well as a great deal of bridge and station wrok.[19] It is also interesting to note that Bernhard Samuelson, the Banbury agricultural engineer, founded his successful business on experience and profits made in France from the manufacture of Ransomes' railway material under licence.[20]

It seems that this extra activity underlay the decision to build the Orwell Works, as a means both to increase production and to separate May's activities from the largely agricultural ones of William Worby, the works manager. The transfer of business began in 1841 and was completed in 1849 when the firm was established in a new works on the dockside.[21] The dual role of the firm was expressed in the motto adopted for the grand dinner to mark the complete transference—"Success to the Plough and Rail". Financially, railway work was of tremendous importance but it also brought the first real experience of mass production techniques (utilised to the full in the manufacture of wooden trenails where "the highest degree of division of labour" was introduced),[22] and the use of specialised machinery. It is also known that one of Ransomes' earliest steam engines was made for Thomas Brassey, perhaps indicating that the railways rather than agriculture may have prompted the firm's original interest in steam engineering.[23]

The 1830's also witnessed the beginnings of lawn mower production.[24] Ransomes began manufacturing the original Budding design under licence in 1832 and by 1852 had produced some 1,500 machines, incorporating some improvements. It is difficult to classify this activity but for most purposes it is convenient to include it in the non-agricultural category, especially in view of its later independence within the business. A very astute move in the long term, lawn mower manufacture was yet another buffer between the firm and the unpredictable fortunes of agriculture.

The overwhelming impression gained from contemporary descriptions is one of emphasis on non-agricultural work and there is some indication that the agricultural implement side of the business may have been relatively neglected. In the 1840's when George Biddell joined the firm, the principal work in this sphere was in fairly rudimentary products such as Gardner's

3

turnip cutter and a range of plough irons, although some effort was being put into thrashing machines which were becoming popular at this time with the tightening up of the agricultural labour market.[25] Ransomes did, however, recognise the increasing interest in agricultural technology and the potential value of the Royal Agricultural Society shows and the firm was the leading exhibitor at the Oxford Show in 1839, with more than six tons of implements and machinery, including ploughs, chaff cutters, Biddell's scarifier and a thrashing machine.[26] In 1841 it exhibited a steam thrashing machine driven by a portable engine and in the following year the first agricultural self-moving (traction) engine.[27] The output of these novelties is difficult to estimate but there is no doubt that by 1850 Ransomes had the technical expertise and labour force to undertake skilled work. In the 1850's a large amount of delicate instrumentation was made for the Greenwich Observatory.[28] How far this activity was a spin-off from techniques developed in non-agricultural work, or, indeed, financed from profits made from railway contracts, may never be known.

While less emphasis may have been put on agricultural work, Ransomes remained in close touch with farmers' requirements. The "Y.L." series of ploughs, which enjoyed a long reign of success, was devised following a complaint from a customer in 1843.[29]

Another feature of the pre-1851 period is the conscious effort to cultivate export markets, a feature which had long-term consequences of inestimable value. The firm was not slow to profit from the wave of emigration which followed the peace of 1815. Emigrants were encouraged to take Ipswich-made implements with them and some degree of success was recorded in Canada, Australia and other areas of colonial expansion.[30] The primary markets for exports at this early stage appear to have been British Possessions.

Largely, it seems, under the impetus of the first railway-building boom, the firm grew by leaps and bounds. By 1849 the total workforce was well over 1,000,[31] and steam engine manufacture, which was to dominate future production, was becoming established.[32] The application of steam to agriculture was encouraging the growth of other specialist firms, notably Clayton and Shuttleworth of Lincoln, Garretts of Leiston, and Burrells of Thetford. Prior to this departure some idea of Ransomes' range of agricultural products can be obtained from an 1844 catalogue,[33] its first comprehensive item of trade literature. Ploughs had pride of place with wooden and iron varieties and Biddell's scarifier appears to have been the next best selling line. Added to these were horse rakes, rollers, turnip cutters, grain crushers, thrashing machines and horse-works. The catalogue, of course, is no guide to the actual numbers manufactured, but the subsequent widening of the range of products advertised seems to indicate a revival of interest in the agricultural side of the business in the 1840's.

The Drive to Maturity: 1851–1875

In 1851, the year of the Great Exhibition, Ransomes was still not firmly committed to any particular range of products. Although Charles May left the firm in that year or soon after, railway and other non-agricultural work continued to be of vital importance throughout the 1850's and several other ideas were implemented, notably the construction of an iron steamship at Ipswich.[34] There is an increasing indication, however, that a long term move towards agriculture was being made. This is understandable in view of the improved reliability of the agricultural market at this time. Lord Ernle's "golden age" was in full swing and something of a mania for mechanisation was developing so that agricultural engineering could do little other than benefit from the mood of the times. In the third quarter of the nineteenth century the dearth of documentation gives way to a mass of material indicating a sustained and vigorous demand for farm implements and machinery of all kinds at home and abroad. Throughout the 1850's and 60's Ransomes expanded its agricultural engineering at the expense of other activities, a direct reversal of the policy pursued between 1815 and 1835.

The most significant outcome of this trend was the transference of all railway material manufacture to a new firm, Ransomes and Rapier, in 1869. This was done primarily to expand the

4

capacity for agricultural work, especially steam engines and thrashers. There may, however, have been more behind the decision, as railway building had slumped in 1866, hitting Ransomes' customers hard at the same time as "chilled iron" was being superseded by steel in the manufacture of railway parts, to the disadvantage of the Ipswich firm. The loss of almost all contemporary records relating to railway work, presumably on the formation of Ransomes and Rapier, tends to exaggerate the firm's earlier commitment to agricultural implements and machinery when it really played a secondary role, but it is important to emphasise the re-emergence of this side of the business. By 1851 Ransomes had a national reputation and was a leading member of the select group of East Anglia businesses which was to dominate the agricultural engineering industry for the rest of the century.[35]

While ploughs and field implements continued to be an important element, the dominant feature of this period is Ransomes' success in exploiting the new enthusiasm for the use of steam power in agriculture. A major contributor to this area was John Head, apprenticed to the firm in 1848,[36] whose technical skill helped produce some of the most reliable and efficient engines, and another was the works manager, William Worby, who collaborated with John Fowler in the early days of steam ploughing. Despite early involvement, however, Ransomes gave up its interest in steam ploughing soon after Fowler set up his own works in 1862.[37] Much of the firm's steam engineering was directed towards producing engines for other purposes, notably thrashing and barnwork, developing first the portable engine which had to be moved around farms by horses and later the more sophisticated self-moving (traction) engine which proved more popular with British farmers and contractors because it could also be used for haulage and a variety of other tasks of a less seasonal nature, a preference which became more marked after 1880 when falling profits demanded a more efficient use of plant and machinery.

The harnessing of steam power for agricultural purposes was perhaps the outstanding achievement but by 1860 most agricultural implements and machines had undergone some form of improvement notably in the substitution of iron for wood in their manufacture, a change which did a great deal to establish a specialist agricultural engineering industry in the place of a multitude of local craftsmen. In 1864 Ransomes introduced its "Newcastle" series of ploughs which enjoyed a great reputation, perhaps somewhat artificially enhanced by the employment of James Barker who specialised in winning ploughing matches with them.[38] Harvesting machinery was briefly manufactured by the firm in the 1860's but then dropped, a wise move as competition at home was fierce and was otherwise dominated by American machines. Where Ransomes enjoyed probably its highest reputation was in the manufacture of thrashing machines which from 1850 onwards became progressively more efficient and capable of finishing as well as thrashing the grain.

The 1860's also witnessed a considerable upsurge in overseas trade, initially in ploughs and the simpler field implements but then in steam engines and thrashers. A spectacular but short-lived boom took place in the Egyptian trade during the American Civil War when Egyptian cotton production was massively expanded, but a more lasting market opened up with the expanding grain areas of Eastern Europe. Trade with Western Europe was also brisk, helped by a spate of international exhibitions and this lasted until the late '70's and '80's when tariff barriers were imposed to protect domestic manufacturers. Ransomes was not slow in developing its export potential and a series of foreign catalogues began to appear to help make the firm's products better known. Specialised products also became part of the firm's output, aimed specifically at export markets. Of these the most successful was the Head and Schemioth straw-burning apparatus[39] which enabled agricultural engines to be used in countries where mineral fuel was scarce, opening up a new range of markets which included the Russian Steppes and South America.

By 1871 the works had extended from its original 6 acres to an area of 10 acres,[40] much of this extra space being given over to steam engine and thrasher production. As well as shedding the railway work to Ransomes and Rapier, the firm increased its commitment to agriculture by transferring the whole of its manufacture of food-preparing machinery to Hunts of Earls

Colne,[41] thus reinforcing the pattern of diversification in times of depression and specialisation during a boom.

Growth in Adversity: 1875–1914

The last quarter of the nineteenth century is recognised as being a period of depression in British agriculture, especially in the arable sector, the main market for implements and machinery. There is, however, little indication that this adversely affected Ransomes' general development and even during the worst years of the middle 1880's a work force of around 1,500 was regularly employed.[42] The secret of this continued success lies in the firm's export interests, which more than compensated for losses at home. Indeed, in times of deepest gloom British agricultural engineers were accused of deepening the depression at home by supplying competitors overseas with the machinery to flood the country with cheap grain! Leaving aside such considerations, it was the export trade which was the dominating feature of Ransomes' history up to 1914.

It is fortunate that output figures exist from 1871 onwards and a clear pattern emerges for most departments of the Orwell works of stagnation at home (at least before 1900) and expansion overseas.[43] Reproduced in graph form the fortunes of the firm very closely correspond with the fluctuations of the export market. At home, it seems, agriculture had by 1880 already reached saturation level for machinery, a trend which was accelerated by a declining arable acreage. The only significant growth seems to have been in ploughs and harrows, lawn mowers and general foundry work, together with some of the more elaborate forms of steam engine. British farmers increasingly relied on machinery contractors rather than buy the full range of equipment and have a great deal of it lying idle out of season. The main development in the home market was in the non-agricultural sphere, but at the same time the range of alternatives was restricted by competition from well-established specialist engineering firms. Ransomes, however, had some options still open. Lawn mower production was given a new footing with the establishment of a separate works in 1872 which signalled rapid progress and the regular launching of new and successful models.[44] Much of the firms' domestic steam engineering effort was aimed at road haulage, although this market continued to be hampered by restrictive legislation, and to a lesser extent fixed industrial engines. The period saw also experiments with oil engines and some interesting but short-lived excursions into tractor manufacture.[45] Otherwise, the main developments within home production were in quality and variety rather than quantity.

The firm's fortunes were inextricably bound up with foreign markets, demands coming from a continually developing colonial sector, particularly Australasia, and from Eastern Europe, where expansion in arable farming for the world grain market corresponded with the abolition of serfdom, creating the necessity to mechanise on a grand scale. In the organisation of these overseas markets a clear trend is discernible over the period. Early informal contacts through British merchant houses were replaced by branch warehouses, in Ransomes' case, especially in Eastern Europe. These were found later to be sometimes more conveniently handled as agencies, in a similar way as at home, with local men taking on the responsibility of developing trade. The firm's interest in overseas trade from 1870 onwards is indicated by the frequent business trips abroad by prominent members of the firm and by the lavish entertainments laid on for prospective foreign buyers at the Orwell works.[46] Surviving publicity shows the firm's concern to produce catalogues and other material in all the major foreign languages. Following the pattern set at home Ransomes took part, very successfully, in the main international industrial exhibitions.

In 1899 a very impressive collection of 107 gold medals, 80 silver, 5 bronze and 3 major decorations was assembled into a permanent exhibition case and facsimile copies issued to several branches.[47] By 1900, however, the value of international exhibitions was declining and posters and catalogues were achieving comparable results. The archival collection is particularly rich in trade catalogues which reflect the world-wide interests of the firm in a variety of languages—

6

Arabic, Bulgarian, Dutch, Esthonian, French, German, Greek, Hungarian, Italian, Lettish, Polish, Portuguese, Rumanian, Russian, Spanish, Swedish and even Welsh.

The visible pattern of exporting up to 1913 is one of balanced growth but this conceals many subtle changes of emphasis. For instance, the balance of colonial and foreign markets appears to be fairly constant but within each sector changes took place. Colonial trade in 1875 was mainly with Australasia, but thereafter this market dwindled in importance in the face of American and Canadian competition and the growth of an effective native industry more closely geared to the area's needs. This downward trend, however, was offset in the longer run by rapid growth in South Africa, where the firm was quick to seize the opportunities, initially for industrial machinery during the gold rush, and later, for agricultural machinery immediately after the Boer War, and to a lesser extent in India where "improved" native ploughs were much in demand. In non-colonial markets a similar pattern of internal adjustment operated with a decline in Western European markets, following tariff restrictions, being offset by a regular trade with Russia and dramatic activity in South America where in 1893, for example, one customer alone ordered 143 thrashing machines and 137 engines.[48]

The trend in products for export balanced itself, though less successfully, with an increasing emphasis on thrashing machines and portable engines. By the turn of the century most of the major overseas markets had their own industries producing the more rudimentary implements while America and Germany were fierce competitors, the former especially in harvesting machinery. Britain retained its leadership in high quality heavy agricultural machinery and Ransomes expended a great deal of energy in perfecting thrashers for the Russian market. There was still, however, an outlet for ploughs in the less agriculturally developed countries in British Africa and Ransomes exploited this to the full in the decade or so before the outbreak of the first world war.

After 1900 British agriculture revived somewhat and this, coinciding with an export boom, helped to make the first decade of the twentieth century a period of unprecedented prosperity. Home trade improved by around 40 per cent and the export trade by some 130 per cent. This was linked with a new building programme and by 1907 the firm was well equipped with some of the most advanced machine tools. The surviving engine dispatch books show year after year of record sales figures and the trend was still very much upwards at the outbreak of war.[49] Russia was still a considerable importer of Ransomes' machinery, much of it through the firm's Odessa branch and many accounts were still outstanding when the business was lost at the Revolution.[50]

In 1884 the firm became a private limited company and in 1911 it was successfully launched as a public company with a share capital of £750,000. Between 1901 and 1910 its profits annually averaged over £63,000 against assets of £844,000. Income was dominated by exports which in some classes of machinery ran at about 98 per cent of production in 1913.[51]

The First World War

Up to 1914 it can be claimed that the history of Ransomes had been one of fairly continuous progress, the worst effects of economic fluctuation having been tempered by internal readjustments. The outbreak of war, however, created a totally artificial situation in which overseas markets were lost overnight and the national war effort over-rode all other considerations. Almost immediately 30 per cent of the workforce was lost to the armed forces and by the October of 1914 the first substantial contract from the war office, for 250 wagons, had been received. For the next four years production at the Orwell works was absorbed by war contracts and in common with many other major employers, Ransomes, for the first time, took on a large number of women manual workers. By the end of the war some 2,000 women were engaged on munitions contracts.

The many-sided nature of the firm's pre-war production, varying from the nut-and-bolt simplicity of some farm implements to the engineering complexities of the thrashing machine and steam engine, meant that Ransomes was able to undertake a wide variety of war work within its different departments. Wagons and carts were, in fact, a straightforward adaptation of pre-war work while other goods, particularly in the field of munitions, could utilise some of the machine tools and assembly procedures used for engine parts, etc. During the course of the war Ransomes munitions output was one million shrapnel shell case forgings, 440,000 shell cases, three million shell and fuse components, 610,000 units of practice shot, 1,700 mines, 1,500 mine sinkers, 10,000 Stokes gun bombs, and 400 sets of chemical smoke apparatus for ships. Weaponry was not a major consideration but the firm did manufacture some 225 trench howitzers. In 1916 even greater demands were made on the firm when it was asked to manu- facture aeroplanes. A new factory was constructed for this purpose and the first aircraft, an FE2b was completed early in the following year. In the short remaining period of the war nearly 800 aircraft were built, a considerable achievement for a firm with no previous experience in this brand of technology. In association with aircraft production a total of 650 airship- and kite-balloon sheds and aircraft hangars was made together with 3,800 bombs.[52]

Government contracts certainly seem to have been most prominent in the minds of those who ran the firm.[53] Yet at the same time they were under pressure not to neglect their agri- cultural commitments. British agriculture was given an abrupt stimulus by the fears and realities of blockade to produce as much food as possible. Consequently, demand for agricultural machinery, which had only just begun to revive, leapt dramatically. Labour shortages (some real and some imagined) encouraged farmers to invest in more machinery. Most classes of agricultural machinery continued to be supplied, albeit in smaller quantities, and the war saw also the first widespread use of the motor tractor. Ransomes had experimented earlier with tractors but never on a commercial scale. In fact Britain's wartime tractors were largely provided by Henry Ford. The experience of Ransomes would seem to suggest that any spare capacity in British agricultural engineering was more than taken up by war contracts so that the oppor- tunity to establish a viable British tractor industry was never exploited.

Manufacturing conditions such as those which prevailed between 1914 and 1918 were artificial and such developments as occurred were at best only indirectly related to the industry's real role. The vital importance of the war was in its effects on the international economy. With the return to normality Ransomes was suddenly faced with trading conditions such as it had never before experienced, and which were to prove its greatest challenge.

Between the Wars

The return to peace did not, however, signal a continuation of the boom which had charac- terised the years immediately before 1914. In fact there was a short busy period up to 1920, although a woodworkers' strike in 1919 led to the loss of £47,000 worth of thrasher production, and a number of recklessly over-optimistic post-war orders were cancelled.[54] Circumstances had changed considerably during the four years of war, so much so that a complete re-appraisal of firm's business role was necessary. As has been pointed out, trade had been export-led since the 1870's and Ransomes' prosperity was determined by fluctuations in world demand. Specifi- cally, two of the firm's most prominent overseas markets were lost or severely weakened. The loss of Russian trade incurred as a result of the 1917 revolution was devastating and irrecoverable, as at one stroke the firm's prime foreign customer was removed. Equally worrying but less dramatic was the erosion of the South American trade by U.S. competition which had a free run in war time. Added to this, at home, agriculture stagnated after the repeal of the Corn Production Act in 1920. Thus, paradoxically, now that the firm was free to resume production of its full range of agricultural wares, demand disappeared. By the end of 1920 the Indian summer of reconstruction was over and orders dried up or were cancelled.

In the industry as a whole the advantages of amalgamation and rationalisation (a feature of competitive U.S. firms a quarter of a century earlier) were soon recognised. Fortunately the firm did not involve itself with the ill-fated Agricultural and General Engineers

8

combine, but instead, in 1919, arranged an exchange of directors with Ruston and Hornsby Ltd., of Lincoln[55] one of the strongest forces in the industry which was beginning to do very well from the manufacture of construction plant and machinery. Under the arrangement Ransomes inherited most of the purely agricultural engineering work, placing the firm in a strong position in relation to its rivals.

Recovery was slow and painful and was based on the two well-tried responses to depression— diversification and exporting. As in the past, non-agricultural products assumed a greater importance and a whole range of new products was introduced. These included bus bodies, trolley buses, fairground amusements, electric vehicles and industrial electric motors as well as precision tools and aircraft hangars.[56] Much of this undoubtedly benefited from the mass-production experience gained during the first world war.[57] Moreover from 1919 onwards lawn mower production was accelerated with special emphasis on light motor mowers for domestic use, and gang mowers for larger works. By 1937 production had to be transferred to larger premises as the original works was unable to handle a range of hand and power mowers unequalled by any other firm in the world.[58]

On the agricultural side, business conditions were hardly favourable at any time before 1939, although Ransomes benefited from the failure of its main competitors in the plough trade, especially Howards of Bedford, whose business it inherited on the failure of A.G.E. Ltd. in 1932.[59] Experiments were being made at this time with tractor-implement linkages, particularly by Harry Ferguson and Ransomes, in the 1920's, expanded its range of tractor-drawn implements, although it took another war finally to establish the motor tractor in British farming.[60] Large quantities of horse rakes were also produced and many can still be seen rusting in farmyards with the name of the firm uncomfortably cast into the iron seat. The association with Ruston and Hornsby Ltd., also meant that in this period binders and mowers were manufactured. In all, a surprisingly complete range of implements and machinery was marketed in the face of diminishing competition from other British firms.

In the export field radical adjustments were necessary following the loss of the Eastern European markets. Fortunately, as in the past, losses in one area were partly offset by gains in another and here South Africa, a market carefully cultivated since the turn of the century, emerged as a major growth point, together with her neighbours, Rhodesia, Kenya and Uganda. For a while also, Western Europe re-opened its doors and branches were established in France and Italy before import tariffs hampered further development. The condition of international trade between the wars meant that a return to anything like the pre-1914 prosperity was out of the question but it does seem that successes in British Africa and, to a certain extent, South America, may have made the difference between Ransomes' survival in agricultural engineering and business failure, such as afflicted many of the other well-known names in the industry between the wars.

One important phase which was finally concluded, however, was the century-old steam era. Some attempt was made to enter the steam wagon market in the 1920's without success, as this was rapidly contracting and competition for dwindling custom was severe. Agricultural demand for steam power lingered on into the 'thirties and one batch of portables was made as late as 1942, although not sold. One or two traction engines left the works up to the early 1940's and others remained in store, disappearing, perhaps for salvage, during the second world war.[61] The future clearly lay with the internal combustion engine but this was firmly in the hands of the motor industry.

The Second World War

Ransomes' contribution to the national war effort between 1939 and 1945 was as considerable in the execution of war contracts and the continued output of agricultural machinery as it was between 1914 and 1918. One significant difference, however, affected the nature of the firm's war work on this second occasion. The dangers of air attack were fully realised and Ipswich, only ten miles inland from the east coast, was rightly regarded as a vulnerable target; indeed some 1,500 raid warnings were given during the course of the war. Production was, therefore, largely limited to parts rather than complete assemblies, although both the range and volume of output were greatly in excess of those during the first war.

War contracts were dispersed throughout the different departments of the works, again to reduce their vulnerability to air attack. The lawn mower works was the most thoroughly reorganised section with production of lawn mowers being stopped almost immediately with the exception of gang mowers for airfields, and the released capacity was given over to high-grade machine tools and a variety of armaments work, including aircraft assemblies, gun and bomb trailers and bomb parts. The thrasher works, containing the principal woodworking and welding shops continued to supply agricultural machinery along with sheet metal and fabrication work for tanks, gun carriages, etc. In addition it produced armaments parts, hangars, and a wide range of other goods. The main execution of high-grade engineering contracts was, of course, dealt with by the engine works where tank parts, aero-engine components and many naval requisites were produced. The firm's prominent place in electrical vehicle construction, established in the inter-war period, also proved useful, around 1,200 trucks being supplied for use at home and abroad.

Only one department, the plough works, retained a semblance of its former identity chiefly because of the "plough-up" policy. Increased home demand for ploughs, thrashers, small tractors (largely used in market gardening) and other implements and machinery was met by much more rigidly imposed standardisation of designs, and, by this means, production was raised to 50 per cent above the pre-war level, despite restrictions on labour, materials and factory space. Some of this increase was secured by sub-contracting to small groups of workers spread around the surrounding villages, a return to the old pre-industrial "putting out" system.[62]

In 1945 Ransomes was faced with the familiar problems of post-war readjustment. Fortunately, these were not complicated by world depression and the return to normality was swifter and less painful.

The Post-War Years[63]

Of prime importance in the recent history of Ransomes was the acquisition, in 1946, of 250 acres of land at Nacton, just outside Ipswich, and the commencement of a complete relocation of activities from the old Orwell site starting with the foundry which was opened in 1948. Immediate post-war demand for implements and machinery provided a platform for what amounted to an ambitious new start and with new buildings and plant the firm embarked on an organisational and technical programme which has now come to fruition. Re-organisation of the existing departments has gradually brought about the conduct of business through four largely autonomous divisions, each handling its own product design, development and marketing although the accounting, computing and research facilities are now centralised. In terms of its range of products the firm's interests remain diverse, output in 1973 being more or less evenly balanced between agricultural and non-agricultural goods, as is indicated by the sales figures for that year:[64]

	£
Tillage equipment division	4,949,000
Harvesting machinery division	2,131,000
Electric truck division	2,759,000
Grass machinery division	5,951,000
Castings for the trade from Ransomes' Foundry	338,000
	£16,128,000

Since the war, and particularly in the last decade or so, changes have been taking place which have altered the balance within and between the various product divisions. There has been greater specialisation and line dropping to make the firm more competitive on a narrower front and this is especially well illustrated in the case of the grass machinery division. Here the post-war years saw the full realisation of the potential of the lawn-mower business, with what had been a useful sideline in times of agricultural depression developing into a distinctive and vital element of the firm's output. Indeed, outside the farming and business community the name of Ransomes is still almost exclusively associated with grass cutting. Recently, however, very considerable real growth has been achieved by concentrating on professional machines, now more than ever in demand as a result of the massive expansion of leisure activities. Garden mowers, for which the firm was justly renowned were finally dropped in the late 1960's and are now only manufactured in Australia, under licence. In those lines on which it now concentrates, however, Ransomes is recognised as a world leader in technology, its principal customers being public authorities, sports organisations and golf courses. Ransomes machines have been used in preparing for many notable sporting events including the recent Olympic Games in Mexico and Germany, and the Masters Golf Tournament in the U.S.A.

The other important non-agricultural development has been the manufacture of electric trucks, another legacy of inter-war diversification which has achieved permanent and growing significance. A wide range of battery electric fork lift trucks, introduced in 1947, and other industrial trucks and tractors has been developed and marketed. Long experience (going back to 1920) and consequent high quality production in this sphere have gained for Ransomes a significant share of the home market and during 1973 an important contract was secured from British Airways for the supply of electric airport tractors, in the face of severe foreign competition.

On the agricultural side many interesting changes have taken place. Immediately following the end of the war the chief priority was the design of new lines and considerable energy was put into revitalising research and development which had been at a standstill for six years. It is evidence of the success of this effort that Ransomes is still widely known for a range of ploughs, harrows, cultivators and other fixed blade tillage equipment. This is in no small part due to the important agreement made in 1946 with the Ford company to manufacture equipment to be used with Ford tractors. The link with a major tractor manufacturer prevented Ransomes from falling behind their rivals as the demand for trailed implements declined. The Ransomes' plough, especially, still has the reputation of a world leader and is perhaps the most commonly used implement of its kind in many countries. The tillage equipment section also kept pace by taking up the manufacture of crop spraying machinery.

Undoubtedly, however, the most dramatic changes have occurred within what is now the harvesting machinery division. After the war probably the most significant necessary adjustment was the phasing out of thrasher manufacture, a mainstay of the business for over a century past. The virtual overnight demise of the thrashing machine in the 1950's was, arguably, the most rapid technological change achieved in British farm mechanisation, the separate reaper and thrasher being replaced by the combine harvester as increasing farm size allowed, and rising labour costs demanded, its belated but now urgent introduction. The first Ransome combines appeared in 1954 and there followed regular refinements which established them firmly on the farming scene. It may, therefore, seem surprising that the firm has recently decided to drop their production but the decision has been taken in response to two separate but complementary factors. Firstly, Ransomes' harvesters, although technically advanced were fairly late in the field and they have never been able to compete internationally with those of the multi-national corporations, notably Massey-Ferguson and International Harvester, which have considerably larger resources for production and, more importantly, marketing and distribution. Secondly, however, the phasing out of combines will release extra capacity for the manufacture of sugar beet and potato harvesting machinery, an interest largely stemming from Ransomes' acquisition of the Johnson and Catchpole companies in 1968. This new departure is benefiting from increasing demand at home and overseas, the Republic of China being a recent customer for potato harvesters. There are interesting precedents for this pattern of product reorientation at other points in the firm's history and by concentrating on more specialised harvesting equipment Ransomes' hopes to dominate what is at the moment a comparatively small market in contrast to grain harvesting where its market share was small and limited by competition from much larger companies.

Exports continue to play a vital role and overseas markets took up over one third of total sales in 1973. Almost every part of the world figures in the firm's export lists and much of this success is due to close study of local conditions and the adoption of products and marketing methods which are appropriate to them. Ransomes has continually enhanced its world-wide reputation in tillage equipment by distinguished performances at the World Ploughing Championships and the firm has been particularly successful with its ranges of ploughs designed both for temperate and dry land conditions. Products, both at home and abroad, are marketed through dealers and distributors and subsidiary companies. In Germany, for instance, grass cutting machinery is sold through a company jointly owned by Ransomes and Landré and Glindermann, of Diemen, a Dutch firm which has been associated with Ransomes for over 100 years. Based in Munster, this marketing company has branches in Hamburg, Frankfurt and Munich. A similar part-ownership system exists in Chile for a company making and selling Ransomes' tillage equipment and disc ploughs aimed at the South American Market. In 1972 a reciprocal marketing arrangement for grass machinery was concluded with Hahn Inc., of Evansville, U.S.A., in which Ransomes has an investment. Much of the firm's output, however, is handled by wholly owned subsidiary companies which operate in Australia, South Africa and France. Over the course of this century the export outlets for Ransomes' products have altered considerably. The emphasis between the wars was on Imperial markets but these have since declined. The pattern now, however, is very interesting as for the first time since the mid-19th century Western Europe has assumed during recent years a very real importance and Ransomes has been quick to exploit the opportunity offered by Britain's membership of the E.E.C. At the same time it is consolidating its position in the Third World where farm mechanisation has great potential and has recently set up Ransomes Overseas Services Ltd. to supply consultancy and management expertise.

In 1974 Ransomes is among the best known and most successful of British agricultural engineers. It also holds a prominent position in British industry as a whole, being well placed in the top one thousand companies and in agricultural engineering ranked below only the U.K. divisions of Massey-Ferguson and International Harvester. Despite its complex and sophisticated organisation, the firm is still overwhelmingly linked with Ipswich, its 130 acre Nacton site (completed by the addition of the recently opened spare parts depot), housing the head office and main factory and employing 2,700 of the firm's total 2,900 workforce. There are, however, other smaller units scattered around the country. A factory at March, in Cambridgeshire, manufactures components for grass machinery and does assembly work for the harvester division. In Tredegar, South Wales, the works of the Steel Case Co. (acquired by Ransomes in 1953) supply steel plate for plough mouldboards and carry out other heat treatment work and future plans aim to make it a self-contained producer of complete mouldboards. Most recently moves have been made to establish a further component works at Doncaster in order to make the company less dependent on sub-contractors. In addition, there has been an interesting spin-off in land development generally. In 1972 Ransomes Property Developments Ltd. was set up to exploit about 120 acres of surplus land at Nacton for warehousing and other industrial premises and the old Catchpole site near Bury St. Edmunds is being developed for housing by another subsidiary, Hepworth Road Developments Ltd.

Conclusion

To have been active almost two hundred years in essentially the same line of business is no small achievement and the history of Ransomes usefully charts the development of agricultural engineering from village craftsmanship into a factory industry. Other firms, it is true, have survived but only by shedding their attachments to agriculture. Garretts of Leiston, Marshalls of Gainsborough, and Rustons of Lincoln are with us as subsidiaries of larger groups but none would now describe itself as agricultural engineers. Ransomes' capacity for survival is a major distinguishing feature, attributable to efficient management, plus some good fortune. In retrospect the firm has been fortunate in its continuous leadership in plough design and manufacture since the days of the first Robert Ransome, as this activity has been in many ways the backbone of its activities. At the same time it has always had a variety of pursuits to tide it over in particularly difficult times and has never made the fatal error of becoming too heavily committed to one range of products. For example, the firm did not become significantly involved in the manufacture either of steam ploughs or harvesting machinery despite the initially tremendous prospects offered by both. It thus avoided the later problems of readjustment which damaged Fowlers of Leeds in the first field, and Samuelsons of Banbury in the other.

While never over-specialising the firm did seem to know when to diversify and when to concentrate its production on a more limited range. A common feature throughout has been its ability to spread its involvements in times of agricultural depression to take in, for example, civil engineering after 1815, railway work around the middle of the century, industrial machinery and large scale exporting from the 1870's onwards and a whole new range of activities in the inter-war years. At the same time, buffer products, especially the manufacture of lawn mowers, have been developed to give more long term security. In times of agricultural expansion it has been equally successful in recognising the need to change direction—as witness the off-loading of railway work to Ransomes and Rapier and food preparing machinery to Hunts to create factory space. This capacity to adapt to changing economic conditions has also been mirrored in its trading policy, especially with overseas custom. Ransomes is a good example generally, and certainly the best within its own industry, of a firm whose continued progress has been the result of maximum flexibility in product-mix and market orientation.

As an example of the agricultural engineering trade as a whole it must be admitted that its greater relative success and its market leadership make it typical only of the higher echelons of the industry. There is sharp dichotomy in the experiences of the international company and the small local firm which, for one reason or another, failed to make the first division. The latter often lacked non-agricultural interests at vital periods and responded to depression by over-specialising or by becoming a maintenance or sales agency for one of the larger firms. Very concentrated specialisation could sometimes work over a considerable period of time, as was the case with Smyths of Peasenhall and its one-product output, and could even bring international recognition, but in the long-term it could not provide a broad enough base to meet every contingency. At the other end of the scale there emerged over the nineteenth century a distinct sector of leading firms, few in number but of international repute, which were the basis of the first agricultural engineering industry in the world. Generally speaking, those firms of mid-century origin were launched immediately on the manufacture of machinery. Ransomes, though, served a long apprenticeship in implement manufacture before it began serious machine building in the 1830's.

Always recognised as a leader in agricultural engineering Ransomes also displays many features typical of the industry as a whole. Its location, in a predominantly rural area, far removed from its sources of raw material but close to the market for its finished products, is common to its most important contemporaries. Most were located not in the heartlands of the Industrial Revolution but in eastern and southern England. Only one firm of note defies this rule—Fowlers of Leeds—and the extent of its commitment to agriculture is debatable. Elsewhere the inextricable identification of the firm with its town of origin (and vice versa) is undeniable and the habit of referring to Howards of Bedford, Taskers of Andover, Bamfords of Uttoxeter, etc., is no mere convenient historian's shorthand. In a very real sense the firm (in the nineteenth century, at least) dominated the town—Ransomes was Ipswich and Ipswich was Ransomes. Nowhere is this more clearly illustrated than in the case of Garretts where the fortunes of the company determined the development of the small village of Leiston, where it was the only significant non-agricultural employer.

In other senses too, Ransomes is a useful representative case study. Even the most superficial approach to the firm's history, via its catalogues and other publicity material, shows the growing range and complexity of products manufactured by the agricultural engineering industry especially during the steam boom in the 1850's and '6o's. Despite necessary excursions into other fields, it is possible to see through Ransomes the emergence of a specialised branch of the engineering industry devoted to the service of agriculture, often indeed having considerably more in common with the farming community than with fellow engineers. There is, in fact, much to indicate that agricultural engineering was a branch of agriculture rather than an offshoot of manufacturing industry.

Such records as exist for other firms in the industry do tend to bear out the major trends illustrated by the development of Ransomes. The switch to non-agricultural work in times of depression is a case in point, as is the overwhelming importance of the export market between 1870 and the Great War. This latter feature deserves emphasis as the performance of British industry generally has often been criticised in that period. If Ransomes is typical, then the agricultural engineering industry was well aware of the potential of overseas markets and well geared to exploit them through specially designed products, vigorous advertising and organised commercial travelling. The relatively small impact of imported agricultural machinery before 1914, with the single exception of harvesting machinery, also indicates a continuing satisfactory performance in the home market, helped no doubt by a comprehensive network of local agencies. It is clear also, that Ransomes and its contemporaries valued the publicity afforded by agricultural shows at home and abroad, during the nineteenth century, although by 1900 it was being claimed that show organisers benefited more from the presence of the large firms than did the firms by their patronage.

It is a great pity that so much archival material was lost in the inter-war years which bankrupted so many of the prominent names in agricultural engineering, but from the historian's point of view the survival of Ransomes is doubly fortunate in that the firm spans the whole development of the industry and also has such a comprehensive set of records. No one would argue that the complete history of the firm, still less of agricultural engineering, could be written from these archives but it could hardly be attempted without reference to them. That British agricultural engineering was a major contributor to agricultural development throughout the world and of considerable significance in the economy of a number of country towns is indisputable, but it is still one of the great neglected fields of British economic history. The opportunity for a wide variety of studies, business, technological, social and economic, is conveyed perhaps by this brief survey of the history of this one leading firm.

References

Unless otherwise stated all references refer to the Ransomes Collection and are prefixed by the Depositor Indicator TR RAN.

1. SP4/6
2. SP1/1 A2
3. CO5/1
4. *Norwich Mercury*, April 23rd 1785
5. *The History of Engineering in Ipswich*, Ipswich Engineering Society, Ipswich, 1950, p. 34
6. SP4/217, pp. 1–2
7. W. Marshall, *Rural Economy of Norfolk*, vol. 1, 1787, pp. 53–54; SH3/48
8. CO5/3
9. P1/A1
10. AC6/1 Section v
11. AC6/1
12. AC6/1 Section vii
13. AC6/1 Section vi

14. SP1/1 A13
15. See, E. L. Jones, *Seasons and Prices*, 1964, pp. 41–42, for the effects of weather on the demand for plough shares
16. AC7/9
17. MP3/1; ET1/1; A. Helps, *Life and Labours of Mr. Brassey*, new edition 1969, pp. 45–46
18. P1/A6 Item ix
19. SP1/1 C14
20. SP4/217, p. 8
21. SP2/95–97; AD4/1
22. SP3/187
23. MP1/6
24. P1/A1 42–43; SP3/124
25. SP4/217, p. 10
26. *Ransomes "Royal" Records*, Ransomes, Sims & Jefferies Ltd., Ipswich, 1939, pp. 16–18
27. SP1/1 C
28. SP3/196
29. MP1/50
30. P1/A1, pp. 13–15
31. AD3/3
32. *Illustrated London News*, January 13th 1849
33. P1/A2, p. 46
34. CO1/2; SP1/1 1D
35. *Great Exhibition Reports of Juries*, London, 1852, pp. 225–242
36. AD3/15
37. TR FOW CO5/(Fowler Collection)
38. SP1/1 E79; SP1/1 K163
39. SP1/1 F27; ET2/7
40. SP1/1 F11
41. SP1/1 F6
42. AD3/5
43. AD7/17
44. SP3/125
45. SP1/1 K122
46. SP1/1 G10, 35B
47. SP1/1 G87
48. SP1/1 H12
49. MP2/194–202
50. AC8/5; AC9/6
51. CO2/1; CO2/2; CO2/7
52. For records relating to Ransomes during the Great War, see, SP1/1 L; AD4/4; AD3/11; PN 7162
53. SP1/1 M49–65
54. SP1/1 M9–48, 98–131
55. AD1/1; SP1/1 M67–74
56. SP1/1 M140, 182; SP1/4
57. SP1/1 M65
58. AD7/16
59. P2/B13–32
60. Ransomes however had begun manufacturing steam traction implement linkages *c*. 1904. In 1907 they also produced the RSM and YLMA ploughs specifically for use with motor tractors (see, MP1/50–51)
61. MP1/19; MP1/32
62. AD5/6; PN 14240G
63. Much of this section is based on information supplied by Mr. G. W. Bone, Managing Director, and Mr. B. Mee, Personnel Director, of Ransomes, Sims and Jefferies Ltd., and by Dr. E. J. T. Collins of The Institute of Agricultural History, University of Reading
64. Ransomes, Sims and Jefferies Ltd. Report and Accounts 1973, p. 8

SELECT BIBLIOGRAPHY

Books and pamphlets

AYTON, Frank, *Applications of engineering to agriculture*. London: Institution of Mechanical Engineers [1926?].
> A short resume of the development of engineering practice dating from 1785, detailing the aims and shortcomings of early machines. Excerpt of the *Proceedings of the Institution of Mechanical Engineers* for the meeting held in Ipswich, June 15th 1926.

AYTON, Frank, *The electric automobile for commercial use: a paper read before the Royal Automobile Club, Wednesday, May 14th 1919*. London: Association of British Motor and Allied Manufacturers Ltd. [1919?].

AYTON, Frank, *Electric vehicles for brewery service*. London: printed by Harrison & Sons [1920?].
> On the cost, reliability and limitations of electric vehicles compared with horse traction and motorised transport. A paper read before the Institute of Brewing on January 12th 1920. Reprinted from the *Journal of the Institute of Brewing*, v. 26, no. 3 (v. 17, new ser.), March 1920, pp. 113–133.

AYTON, Frank, *The use of electric vehicles for municipal purposes*. London: printed by Adlard & Son and West Newman Ltd. [1921?].
> Electric transport compared with that driven by steam or internal combustion engines to prove the superiority of the former over the short distance. A paper read before the Public Works, Road and Transport Congress on November 25th 1921.

AYTON, Frank, *The use of electric vehicles in municipal service: report presented by the Electric Vehicles Committee [to the] Incorporated Municipal Electrical Association, June 17th 1915*.
> Numerous references to contemporary experience of motorised transport to show the economic advantages of the alternatives to horse-drawn traction for short haulage work.

BEAUMONT, Anthony, *Ransomes steam engines: an illustrated history*. Newton Abbot: David & Charles, 1972.

BONE, Victor W., *Manufacturing engineering and some lessons of the war*. Ipswich: Ipswich Engineering Society [1919?].
> Mainly concerns the impact of wartime conditions on the labour market and the trend towards greater standardisation and specialisation of output. Presidential address to the Society, November 21st 1919.

HEAD, John, *A few notes on the portable steam engine, with an account of its construction and general adaptation*. London: E. & F. N. Spon [1877?].

HEAD, John, *On the combustion of refuse vegetable substances, such as straw, reeds, cotton stalks, brushwood, megass, etc., under steam boilers*. Edited by James Forrest. London: Institution of Civil Engineers, 1877.
> Excerpt of *Minutes of Proceedings of the Institution of Civil Engineers*, v. 48, pt. 2, session 1876–1877.

HEAD, John, *On the rise and progress of steam locomotion on common roads*. Edited by James Forrest. London: Institution of Civil Engineers, 1873.
> Excerpts of Minutes of *Proceedings of the Institution of Civil Engineers*, v. 36, session 1872–1873.

Ipswich Engineering Society, *The history of engineering in Ipswich*. Ipswich: W. S. Cowell Ltd., 1950.
> Briefly describes the individual histories of a dozen engineering firms, including that of Ransomes, Sims & Jefferies Ltd. Also contains short chapters of Transport in Ipswich; the Fire Brigade; the Port of Ipswich, etc.

LEWIS, R. Stanley, *Eighty years of enterprise, 1869–1949, being the intimate story of the Waterside Works of Ransomes & Rapier Limited, of Ipswich, England*. Ipswich: W. S. Cowell Ltd. [1951].

Memoir of Robert Ransome [junior]. London: Institution of Civil Engineers, 1866.

A brief obituary. Excerpt from the *Annual Report of the Institution of Civil Engineers*, December 19th 1865.

Memoirs [of members of the Institution of Mechanical Engineers]. London: Institution of Mechanical Engineers, 1905.

Excerpt of *Minutes of Proceedings of the Institution of Mechanical Engineers, February 1905*. Obituaries include that of James Edward Ransome, pp. 160–161.

The Ransome family: Robert Ransome [the elder]; James Ransome; Robert Ransome [the younger]; James Allen Ransome.

Reprinted from the *Biographical Catalogue of Portraits in the Friends' Institute*, London [1888?].

RANSOME, James Edward, *Double furrow ploughs: a lecture delivered at the Framlingham Farmers' Club, January 22nd 1872*. Ipswich: printed by Henry Knights, 1872.

On the history, advantages and profitability of double furrow ploughs.

RANSOME, James Edward, *Ploughs and ploughing: a lecture delivered at the Royal Agricultural College, Cirencester*. Edinburgh: printed by Thomas Constable, 1865.

Examines the history of the plough, recording biblical references and reproducing figures from ancient Egyptian monuments, etc. After a brief survey of the eighteenth- and nineteenth-century developments in both design and production of ploughs, the author examines the contemporary improvers, describing implements employed at home and abroad. Reprinted from *Practice with Science*, pt. 1, July 1865.

RANSOME, J. Allen, *The implements of agriculture*. London: J. Ridgway, 1843.

A detailed and comprehensive survey of implements used from biblical times. Copiously illustrated.

Periodical and newspaper articles

"Activity at the works of Ransomes, Sims & Jefferies Limited." *Implement and Machinery Review*, v. 51 (1925–1926), pp. 765—766.

"Agricultural mechanics: the Orwell Works at Ipswich." *Dorset County Chronicle and Somersetshire Gazette*. January 20th 1859 and the *Southern Times*, January 29th 1859.

GRACE, David R., "Ransomes—Engineers". *Enciclopedia Biografica degli Sciezianti e degli Inventori*. Mondadori, Milan. (Forthcoming publication.)

"Messrs Ransomes, Sims & Head, agricultural engineers, Ipswich: the Orwell Works and its specialities." *The Agricultural Gazette*, July–August 1875.

Includes detailed descriptions of manufacturing processes in the different departments of the Works.

"The Orwell Works." *The Gardeners' Chronicle and Agricultural Gazette*, April 19th 1862.

RANSOME, Edward Coleby, "British agricultural machinery: development of the agricultural machine". *The Manchester Guardian Commercial*, January 4th 1923.

"Ransomes' new foundry: impressions of the modern and scientifically planned Nacton plant." *Farm Implement and Machinery Review*, v. 75 (1949–1950), pp. 1226–1227.

"Ransomes, Sims & Head's Orwell Works, Ipswich." *Implement and Machinery Review*, v. 6 (1880–1881), pp. 3217–3220.

Contains summary description of processes and machines used in the production of ploughs, thrashing machines, engines and boilers.

"The visit of distinguished foreign and English agriculturalists to Messrs Ransomes & Sims at Ipswich and Westerfield." *Ipswich Express*, August 26th 1862.

"Visit of foreign noblemen and gentlemen to the Orwell Works, Ipswich." *Ipswich Journal*, Saturday, August 23rd, 1862.

"Visit to the Orwell Iron Works, Ipswich." *Bell's Weekly Messenger*, August 30th 1858.

Works published by Ransomes, Sims & Jefferies Ltd.

Description of the Orwell Works, Ipswich, with additional notes and illustrations. Ipswich: 1914. Pub. no. 6534 E.

 From the *Proceedings of the Institution of Mechanical Engineers*, Cambridge meeting, 1913.

Ransomes and the Second World War. Ipswich: 1946. Pub. no. 14240 G.

Ransomes "Royal" records: a century and a half in the service of agriculture. Ipswich: 1939. Pub. no. 13400 H.

The war and after. Ipswich: 1920. Pub. no. 7162.

 A single sheet of information on wartime production changes and on the later adaptation of the plant to electric vehicle manufacture.

Wherever the sun shines . . . 175 years of progress by Ransomes. Ipswich: 1964.

Typescript material in the Ransomes collection

Reminiscences. By George Biddell. Cat. no. TR RAN SP4/217.

 Gives details of the life of Robert Ransome senior and also describes the firm's products for the period 1840–1860.

The history of the Orwell Works, 1774–1928. By C. J. Palmer. Cat. no. TR RAN SP1/1.

The history of the Orwell Works [continued], *1929–1961.* By C. W. H. Cullingford. Cat. no. TR RAN SP1/2.

Between the wars [*1919–1939*]. By L. J. Orvis. Cat. no. TR RAN SP1/4.

The Second World War. By L. J. Orvis. Cat. no. TR RAN SP1/5.

The post-war years [*1945–1965*]. By L. J. Orvis. Cat. no. TR RAN SP1/6.

[*History of Ransomes, 1962–1969*]. By L. J. Orvis. Cat. no. TR RAN SP1/3.

THE RANSOME FAMILY

This Chart shows only those descendants of Robert Ransome who are and have been directly associated with the business

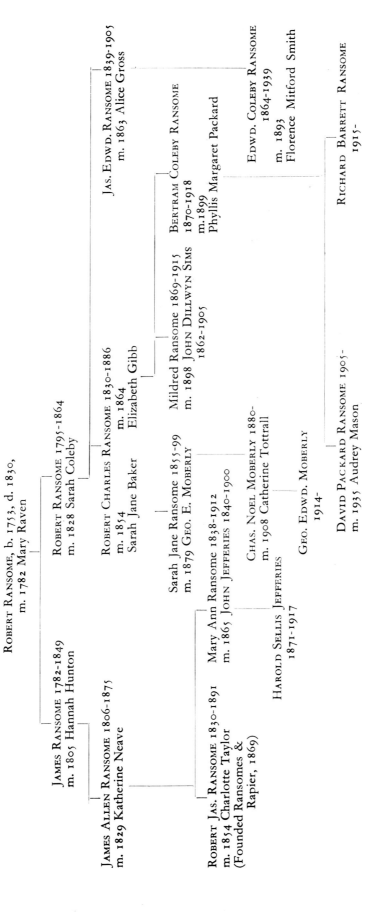

ROBERT RANSOME, b. 1753, d. 1830,
m. 1782 Mary Raven

ROBERT RANSOME 1795-1864
m. 1828 Sarah Coleby

JAS. EDWD. RANSOME 1839-1905
m. 1863 Alice Gross

BERTRAM COLEBY RANSOME
1870-1918
m.1899
Phyllis Margaret Packard

EDWD. COLEBY RANSOME
1864-1939
m. 1893
Florence Mitford Smith

RICHARD BARRETT RANSOME
1915-

JAMES RANSOME 1782-1849
m. 1805 Hannah Hunton

JAMES ALLEN RANSOME 1806-1875
m. 1829 Katherine Neave

ROBERT CHARLES RANSOME 1830-1886
m. 1864
Elizabeth Gibb

Mildred Ransome 1869-1915
m. 1898 JOHN DILLWYN SIMS
1862-1905

ROBERT JAS. RANSOME 1830-1891
m. 1854 Charlotte Taylor
(Founded Ransomes &
Rapier, 1869)

Sarah Jane Ransome 1855-99
m. 1879 GEO. E. MOBERLY

CHAS. NOEL MOBERLY 1880-
m. 1908 Catherine Tottrall

GEO. EDWD. MOBERLY
1914-

DAVID PACKARD RANSOME 1905-
m. 1935 Audrey Mason

Mary Ann Ransome 1838-1912
m. 1865 JOHN JEFFERIES 1840-1900

HAROLD SELLIS JEFFERIES
1871-1917

m. 1854
Sarah Jane Baker

Plate 2. The skittle alley at the rear of Ransome & Son's plough shop in St. Margaret's Ditches (now Old Foundry Road), *c.* 1810. Print of an original watercolour in the possession of the firm (PhN10977).

VISTA PANORAMICA DA FABRICA "ORWELL" EM IPSWICH.

ESTA FABRICA OCCUPA UMA AREA DE 5 HECTARES, E EMPREGA 1,400 OPERARIOS.

A Cidade de Ipswich está a 110 kilometros de Londres, na linha do Caminho de Ferro "Great Eastern," cuja estação em Londres é em Liverpool street. O trajecto faz-se em uma hora e meia.

Plate 3. The Orwell Works from the firm's Spanish steam machinery catalogue of 1891 (PN 2600E).

Plate 4. Aerial photograph of the Nacton site, 1974 (PhN35970).

Plate 5. A section of the new plough and implement shop, Orwell Works, c. 1904 (P2/A 66).

Plate 6.   The finished engine store, Orwell Works, c. 1904 (P2/A 66).

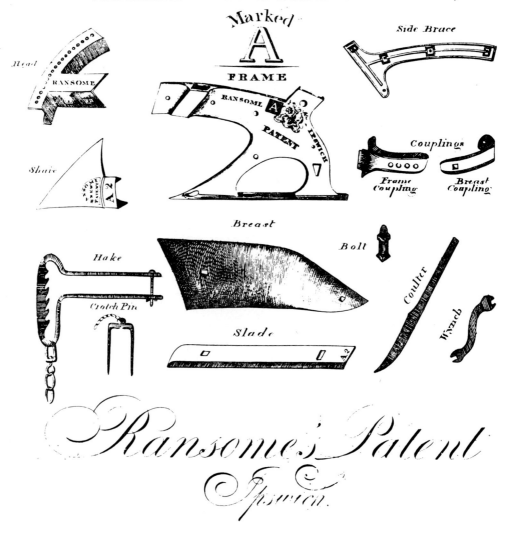

Plate 7. Advertisement for Ransome's interchangeable parts for "A" ploughs, c. 1820. This invention was patented by Robert Ransome Snr. in 1808 (P1/A1 page 36).

BUDDING'S
PATENT
Machine for cutting Grass Plats, &c.

SOLD, BY APPOINTMENT, BY

J. R. & A. RANSOME,

IPSWICH.

THIS Machine is so easy to manage, that persons unpractised in the Art of Mowing, may cut the Grass on Lawns, Pleasure Grounds, and Bowling Greens, with ease. It is easily adjusted to cut to any length; and the beauty of its operation is, that it leaves no seam, nor any of the cut grass upon the Lawn. Other advantages of this Machine are, that the grass may be cut when dry, and consequently it may be used at such hours as are most convenient to the Gardener or Workman,—while the expence of Mowing is considerably lessened, as more than double the work may be done with the same manual labour that is requisite with the Scythe.

Plate 8. Advertisement for Budding's grass cutter, as made by J. R. & A. Ransome, 1844 (P1/A 102).

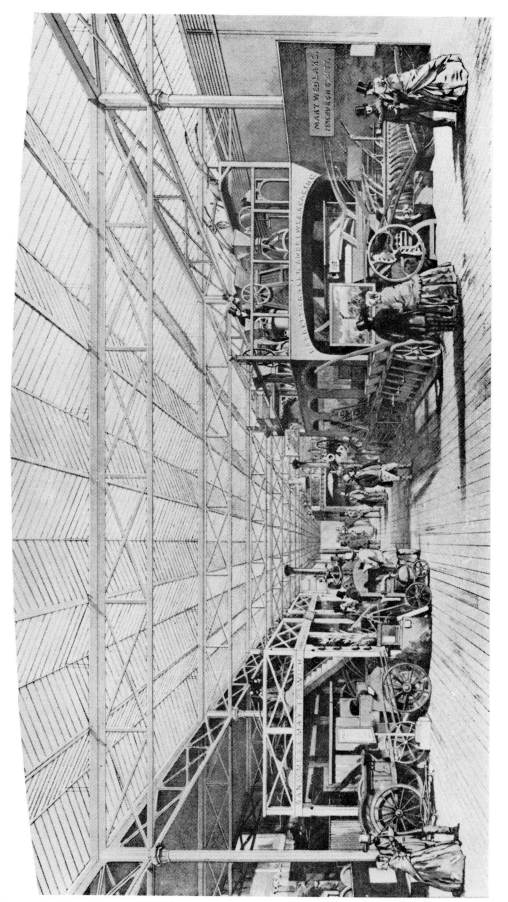

Plate 9. Ransomes & May's display stand at the Great Exhibition, Crystal Palace, London, 1851. Other stands visible are those of Barrett, Exall & Andrewes; Mary Wedlake and Garrett & Sons (MERL 64/121).

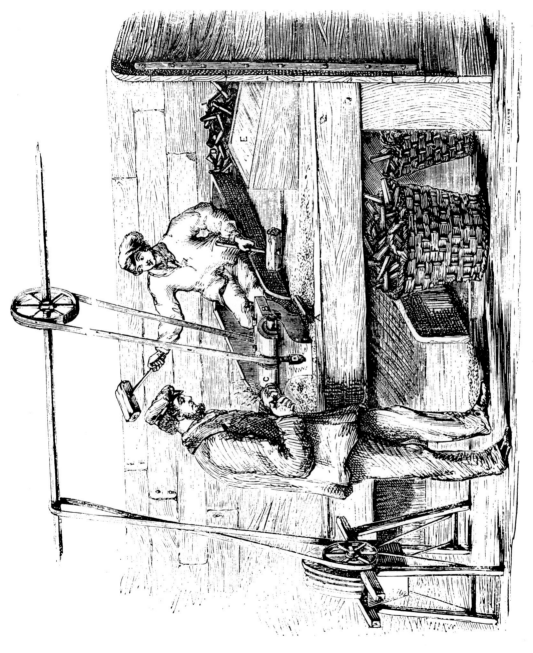

Plate 10. Method of tipping railway trenails at the Orwell Works, 1857, from *The Engineer*, 16 January 1857, p. 42. The trenails secured both the rails to railway chairs and the chairs to sleepers. One man and a boy could produce 1,200 trenails an hour and some 1,186,087 trenails left the works in 1866 alone.

Plate 11. A 20 BHP petrol tractor with 3 furrow plough, invented by J. E. Ransome, 1903. The 4 cylinder vertical motor was built by W. S. Murdoch & W. Beckwith (PhN. 2601).

Plate 12. A section of the aeroplane erecting shop, Orwell Works, 1917 (PhN 4300).

Plate 13. Fleet of fifteen single decker trolley buses as supplied to Ipswich Corporation, 1926. Frank Ayton, Ransomes' works director and an expert on electric vehicles, is at the right of the picture (PhN 6219).

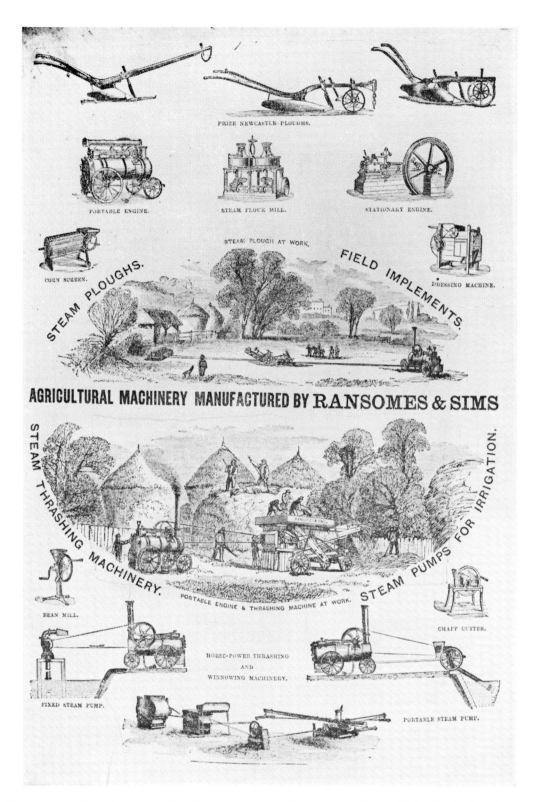

Plate 14. Advertisement for the general product range, late 1860's, including horse ploughs, steam ploughing equipment, portable and stationary steam engines, pumping engines, corn mills, thrashing machines, dressing machines, barn machinery and horse gears. Late 1860's (P8/1 Proof no. 6163).

Plate 15. The foundry employees, Orwell Works, 1889 (SP4/196).

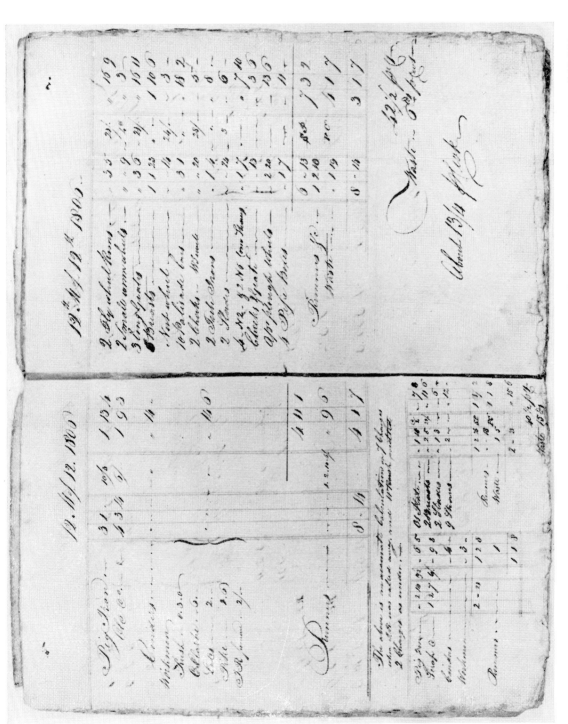

Plate 16. Two pages from James Ransome's account book of his foundry at Great Yarmouth, 1806 (AC6/2).

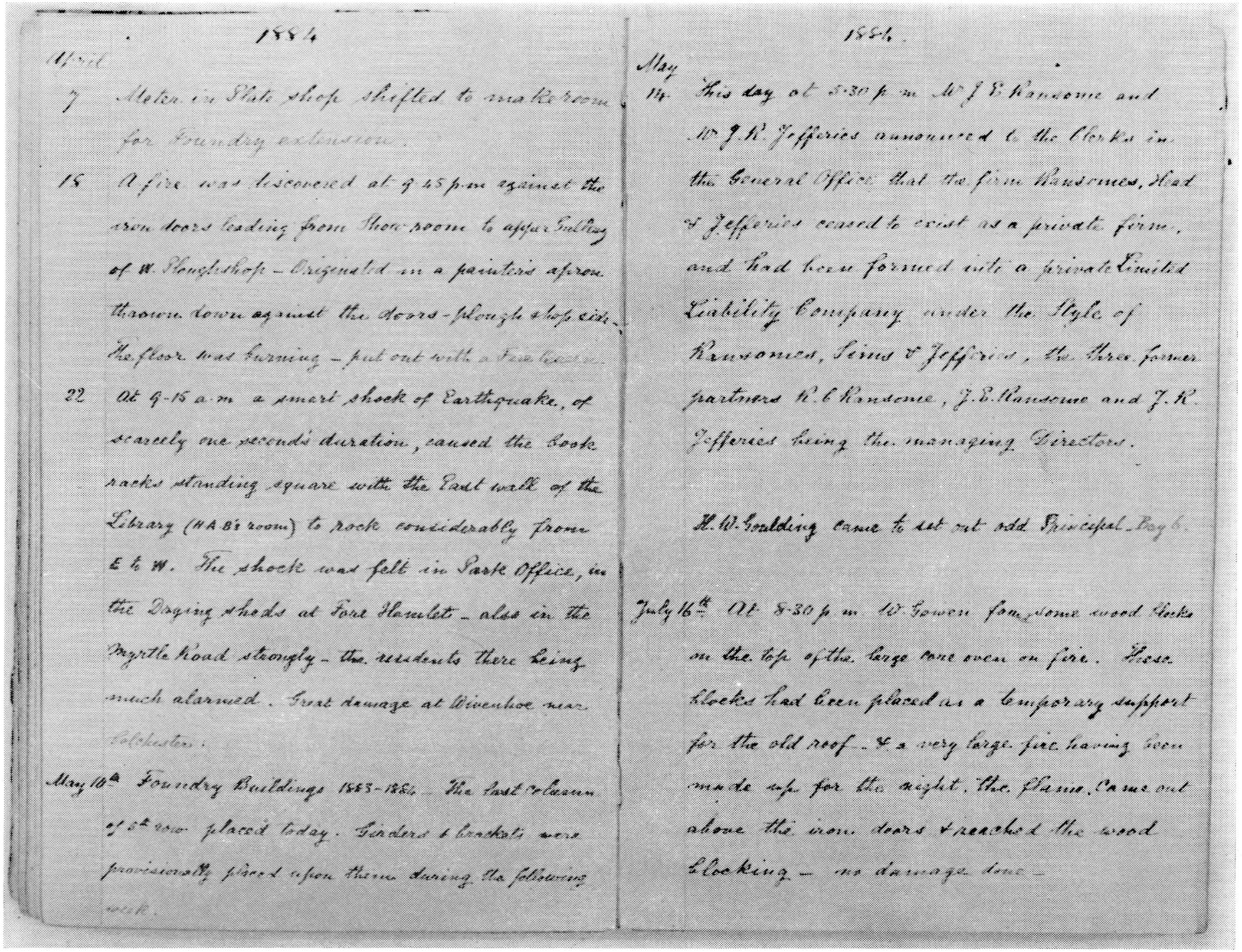

PART TWO

Guide to the Records

THE RANSOMES COLLECTION:
AN ARCHIVAL INTRODUCTION

The historical records deposited by Ransomes, Sims & Jefferies Ltd. at the Institute of Agricultural History are notable for their diversity of type, their extensive coverage of the firm's products and activities and not least their time span, ranging from the late eighteenth century to the present day. Their importance is further emphasised by the fact that only a few major agricultural engineering firms, such as Fowlers of Leeds, Rustons of Lincoln and Garretts of Leiston, preserved similar large bodies of material. All are very diverse accumulations, with an emphasis on graphic, technical and ephemeral material, rather than financial and commercial records. The great majority of other agricultural engineering firms are not nearly so well represented. Large bodies of material have survived for a few smaller firms such as Nalders of Wantage and Hunts of Earls Colne, due mainly to continuity of business in the same premises, but they are atypical of an industry that has witnessed many liquidations, takeovers and amalgamations, especially during the industrial depression between the two World Wars. Indeed, the majority of firms are represented by only a handful of records, mainly publicity material, and much of this was collected by other firms or organisations, such as competitors, agents and research institutions. Private collectors have also accumulated technical and advertising records but usually relating to specific products.

Even so, the Ransomes Collection represents only a small proportion of a veritable mountain of records which must have been generated by this large and complex manufacturing firm. External factors influencing record survival have been the continuity and success of Ransomes as a business since 1789, and only one major change of site—that of the gradual move after 1946 from the Orwell Works in the centre of Ipswich to Nacton, on the outskirts of the town. Internally, the relative lack of any records management policy meant that physical bulk alone militated against the survival of many records, especially during rebuilding or internal reorganisation. There were, fortunately, more conservative forces at work but these were selective with the result that certain types of records, such as summaries or those subject to internal registration, survive better than, for example, routine administrative or accounting records. Internal registration was notably employed for four lengthy records series. These were drawings, photographs, publications and printing block proofs, for which systematic recording was essential for speed of recall and reference. Certain technical records, especially those originating in the engineering department, were also retained to service technical enquiries and facilitate the repair and maintenance of discontinued lines. Finally, a continuous interest in the history and development of the firm, as evinced by C. J. Palmer's *History of the Orwell Works* (SP1/1), and the employment of company historians between 1949 and 1969, meant that the preservation of records became official company policy. As a result most types of record are represented, but a detailed analysis of their composition reveals a far from even pattern of conservation, especially for the earlier period.

The business records proper (CO, AC and AD) comprise useful summary material but exclude the formidable bulk of the subsidiary records. It is possible, especially in view of the paucity of business agreements and patenting records, that more company records (CO) survive, in bank custody, with firms of solicitors or in company strong rooms. The Orwell Works estate records, for instance (CO4), are known to have been transferred to the new owners when the site was sold. As they stand the company records consist of partnership records (CO1), including a few early agreements and the capital ledger 1865–1884; limited company records (CO2) and trade mark records (CO6), including litigation in Chancery 1872–1874 and 1881–1882.

The absence of the long runs of bought ledgers, sales ledgers, cash books, day books and journals in the commercial accounts (AC1–AC4) is compensated for by their summary in the first five private ledgers of RSJ for the period 1884–1944 (AC1/1–5) and the two runs of financial statements 1837–1883 and 1941–1971 (AC7). The cost accounts (AC5) likewise do not survive apart from yearly wage analysis sheets 1871–1939 and two salaries and wages books. However, yearly cost account analysis books were compiled of which those for 1885 and 1936–1939 are preserved (AC5/1–5). Both sets of the accounts are summarised in a director's notebook for 1884–1901 (AC6/5) and a separate volume contains early business accounts 1804–1832 (AC6/1). As the majority of Ransomes' extensive business was done through agents, branch accounting was not significant (AC8). The branch accounts extant are the second volume of financial statements of the Odessa branch 1892–1919, and two general ledgers and two principal journals of the Ipswich town warehouse 1902–1946, which served as Ransomes' immediate retail and wholesale outlet.

The records of the internal governing body of the company, the board of directors (AD1), comprise the first directors' minute book 1884–1937 and the detailed private reports of proceedings at board meetings 1919–1939, which include information on sales, orders, marketing, premises and capital. Less formal summaries (AD2), comprise a director's notebook of sales output and wage statistics 1884–1901 and an engineering department notebook. The breakdown of central administrative records, into those of labour (AD3), premises (AD4) and materials (AD5), means that a once large quantity of material is now represented by a body of records which, though small in number, contains several detailed items. It includes six registers of workmen 1859–1922, a register of apprentices 1838–1872 and a detailed list of workmen in 1835 (AD3); works, plans and maps 1846–1847 (AD4) and two output analysis books 1866–1882 (AD5). According to Palmer's history (SP1/1M) similar output analyses were compiled from 1897 onwards, but have apparently disappeared. Branch administration is principally represented by a regulations book (AD6/1) for the management of the Ipswich and Bury St. Edmunds town warehouses, compiled in 1892.

Commercial records (AD7), concerned with orders, sales and marketing must have comprised an enormous accumulation, especially as they would have included much of the routine business correspondence. General analyses were essential but only a selection now survives. According to Palmer (SP1/1M), two series of export analysis books were once kept from 1863 onwards, one for customers, the other for each different country and also a yearly export diary from 1887 onwards. Although these have not been traced, there are individual export books for Peru and the United States of Columbia 1875–1889; Roumanian agencies 1868–1885 and Russian agencies 1861–1885. There is also a series of yearly sales analyses for 1871–1939 and some useful reference compilations concerning prices, but records of orders are very few, apart from the monthly summaries in the reports of proceedings at directors' meetings (AD1). Agents lists are preserved for the British Isles 1914–1950.

The manufacturing records (MP, DO and ET) are well represented in general, but are unevenly biased towards certain products, notably steam engines. This is probably due to the highly technical nature of such records, their retention for servicing discontinued lines and also to the growth of outside popular interest in steam engineering, especially traction engines. The bias is most noticeable in the records of the manufacturing processes (MP), which refer to the activities of the different departments of the firm. The five most important sections prior to the Second World War were those concerned with steam engineering; thrashing machinery; ploughs and implements; lawn and grass mowing machinery and electric vehicles. (The present

24

division is fourfold—tillage, harvesting, industrial and grass mowing.) Each department (and often sub-department), tended to generate its own records, of which production registers (MP1) are the most prominent.

The majority of manufacturing records were generated by the now defunct engineering department which manufactured its last steam engine in 1942 and ceased to service engines after 1955. These records form a detailed and extensive accumulation. The general engine registers c. 1850–1945 (MP1), are preserved complete and after 1877 consist of two separate series, one arranged by sales number (in order of sale) and the other by manufacturing number (in order of manufacture). There was also a separate series of six detailed traction engine registers, now lost, though their summaries, customer indexes and some detailed register notes survive, as do the detailed oil engine and steam wagon registers. Corn mills were registered independently of other engineering department products and although the register is not extant, the customer index survives.

The engineering department working papers (MP2), show the process of sub-departmental manufacture at work. Individual engine parts and components were made to standard or to order in the turnery (MP2/1–27) and the boiler plates likewise in the boiler shop (MP2/28–29); all components were then assembled by the engine erecting department and the completed engines given manufacturing numbers (MP2/33–4). The engines were tested during and after manufacture by the engine testing department (MP2/35–36), then partially dismantled and packaged (MP2/38–184) and finally dispatched (MP2/194–202). Corn mills also feature in the turnery records, in the reports of dismantling and package and in the dispatch books. There exist also some engineering department parts and servicing records (MP3).

The records of the thrashing machinery department are surprisingly few. (Production was terminated there in 1955 apart from outstanding orders.) The five thrashing machine registers were apparently destroyed in the late 1960's. Customer indexes exist (MP1/45–49), but there are no working papers or parts and servicing records. The plough works records consist of two plough mark registers (MP1/50 and 51), the principal one covering 1839–1943 and four plough and implement parts registers (MP3/14–71), all ceasing in the mid-1950's with the transfer of the plough works from Ipswich to Nacton. It is unlikely that many subsidiary records were kept, but probably there were registers, now lost, of different implement types. The electric vehicle department is represented by two trolley bus production lists 1925–1948 (MP1/53–4). Possibly the records disappeared in the move to Nacton or during the gradual phasing out of electric vehicle production. Finally, the lawn mower works records are not represented at all but as the department remains in production some material may still be with the firm.

The other manufacturing records relate to drawing and design (DO) and experimentation and technical reference (ET). The large number of drawings which were generated required registration from an early date c. 1840 onwards. Eventually different drawings series were introduced, including after 1900, separate departmental series. (The different drawing series are explained in section DO1.) However, their daunting physical bulk proved a constant problem. A memorandum of April 6th 1881 in the front of the first drawings ledger (DO2/1) reads:

"To make some room to store current office and shop drawings we must clean out and destroy all the useless and obsolete drawings."

In October 1893 the following schedule was applied to the existing drawings and entered in the first two drawings ledgers (DO2/1, 2):

D	=	Destroyed
M	=	Missing
R	=	Reserved (of doubtful value)
PI	=	Preserved out of interest

The great majority of ledger entries have "D" codings. Periodic destruction continued there-after, though on a smaller scale. A solution to the problem of size came in the early 1940's when $6\frac{1}{2} \times 4\frac{3}{4}$ inch barcograph transparencies were made of all drawings, initially as a security precaution, but continued thereafter to the present day. A further advantage of the process was that it enabled prints to be made from negative transparencies, thereby allowing the originals to be destroyed, while at the same time facilitating information retrieval.

Very few original drawings and tracings are therefore preserved at the University of Reading. Of the few early "ledger series" drawings to survive, nearly all have the "PI" codings. The only complete survival is the standard list series (DO1/L) of drawings of standard steam engineering components. The barcograph transparencies cover most of the drawing series from the 1880's onwards, including positive transparencies of engineering and thrashing machinery drawings of Ruston & Hornsby Ltd. acquired in the inter-war period. The transparencies were numbered from N1 onwards in order of copying and their registers are still in the custody of Ransomes. The Institute currently holds all transparencies prior to N40,000 relating to the engineering and thrashing machinery departments, some 15,000 in all. Drawing registers (DO2) survive for certain series, together with some subject indexes. These are especially useful when they also record the transparency number.

The experimental and technical reference records (ET), are inevitably a miscellaneous accumulation preserved mainly out of technical interest. Principally they concern steam engineering and thrashing machinery, but include some detailed general compilations on lawn mowers 1830–1911 (ET3/28 and 32) and reapers and mowers 1786–1871 (ET3/12–17). The latter possibly originated from the Hornsby side of Ruston & Hornsby Ltd., of Grantham, which was administered by Ransomes between the two World Wars. The material on plough and implement trials compiled by J. & F. Howard for the period 1905–1915 (ET1/10), probably came into Ransomes' possession when they took over the manufacture of Howard ploughs after that company's liquidation in 1932.

The publicising and promoting of Ransomes products (P), generated substantial quantities of printed records, commencing about 1800, which altogether make up about one third of the entire collection. The period prior to 1846 is covered by two guard albums (P1/A1, 2), but by the late 1850's output had become so vast as to require a system of special registration with publication numbers, which resulted simultaneously in the compilation of mainly annual numerical reference volumes, the majority of which are preserved prior to 1940 (P1/A3–57). Some of the gaps in the series are filled by subsidiary compilations (P1/A58–122) and by in-dividual publications (P2/A and card catalogue). The numbered publications include both advertising material (catalogues, leaflets, testimonials) and servicing literature (instruction books, parts lists), as part of the same numbered series which is still maintained by Ransomes. They are daunting in their quantity, chronology, variety of printing techniques, the range of products to which they refer and, not least, the many different languages in which they are published. Publication registers are preserved for 1931–1958 only (P9/1–2). A fine collection of posters 1882–1930 (P3/1–4), survives in four reference albums, while other publicity records include a selection of semi-current house journals (P4), news releases (P5) and records of advertising campaigns (P7). Production film (P6), has been retained by Ransomes. Records of art work and printing block proofs were also kept in the form of an unbroken run of seventeen reference albums from c. 1850–1969.

Some publicity of Ransomes' competitors and fellow exhibitors appears to have been collected out of general interest and for reference purposes (P/B). Five bound compilations cover the years 1851–1869 (P1/B 1–5), including two volumes of 174 exhibitors' literature, produced for the 1851 Great Exhibition and a selection of Howard publicity for 1851–1930 (P2/B 11–32 and P1/B3), again possibly acquired on Howards' liquidation. Also of note is a 1773–1777 trade catalogue of James Sharp (P2/B51).

The official photographic records (PH), as distinct from the casual acquisition of photographs by the firm (SP), or their secondary use for technical illustration (ET2 and ET3), are well

26

preserved due to registration and the compilation of reference print albums. The main series commencing in 1856, is still maintained by Ransomes and the Institute of Agricultural History has the first twenty-seven albums prior to July 1947 PhN 1–11597 (PH2/1–27). There are, however, no negatives (PH1), their destruction according to a note in the first album, having commenced in 1896. The subsidiary "In Work" series (PH2/28–34) and thrashing machinery series (PH2/35–39), have complete album runs, but the register survives only for the former series (PH4/2).

The retention of a large number of show and exhibition records (SH), is a measure of the firm's pride of achievement. Although 112 certificates are preserved in a variety of languages and art styles (SH1/1–112), the prize register and prize list (SH2/1, 2), indicate that many more awards were won though not retained. The subsidiary records (SH3), are also extensive if miscellaneous in nature. The very large number of social and personal records (SP), belong outside the firm's principal commercial concerns, but they reflect a long and continuing interest on the part of management and employees in the history of a "patriarchal" firm. The preservation and compilation of this material owes a great deal to C. J. Palmer and the company historians, C. W. H. Cullingford and L. J. Orvis. The real encouragement to the generation of such records came with C. J. Palmer's outstanding *History of the Orwell Works 1774–1928* (SP/1), which includes eleven sets of notes, comprising over a thousand pages of typescript and documentary illustration, together with three sets of indexes and summaries. The history was continued for the period 1949–1969 by Cullingford and Orvis (SP1/2, 3), whose yearly desk diaries were a primary source of information (SP1/12–19). The gap between 1928 and 1949 is partly filled by *The Orwell Works Magazine*, a bi-monthly publication, running from 1931 to 1940, which was edited and produced by Ransomes' employees.

The remaining social and personal records are mainly typescript compilations, ephemera, material remitted to the firm, especially to the historian's office and press cuttings, either extracted from local papers or supplied by a cuttings bureau. Among this material can also be found items concerning the early development of the lawn mower which were collected by G. B. W. Scholefield in the 1950's (SP3/121–180).

The Arrangement of the Catalogue

This catalogue is a summary of the detailed typescript catalogue in use at the Institute of Agricultural History. Many of the more detailed or repetitive entries, such as those describing the contents of the bound volumes of the firm's publications (P1) and the collections of ephemera (SP) have been considerably abbreviated. The detailed entries in the typescript catalogue are essential to provide as much information as the user would require in order to determine whether or not to consult the original record, to serve as a basis for subject indexing, such as of products and manufacturers; and, not least, to facilitate the compilation of summary lists and catalogues. Neither catalogue gives full details of the series of the firm's drawings, photographs and publications, each of which runs into many thousands of items. All three series were originally numbered by the firm but as only partial registration is now extant, the information for the individual items has been organised in the form of separate card catalogues arranged in order of the firm's reference number.

The arrangement of the records in this catalogue is according to a classification system based on a "structural model" of the activities and organisation of the firm. This is in contrast to primary arrangement by record type on the one hand, or point of origin within the firm on the other. The former system is not generally favoured by archivists nowadays, typology for its own sake being regarded as a barren exercise, while the latter system creates too many problems if, as is often the case, the source is uncertain.

This situation may be compared with, say, the archives of local government which are the product of a self-perpetuating pattern of internal departmental organisation, reinforced by statutes and regulations or by the development of a bureaucracy. The records of an agricultural engineering firm, on the other hand, result from and reflect its function as a competitive business, whose survival will require constant change and adaptability. Therefore each firm's departmental structure will be distinctive to that firm and changes will occur over time within and between individual departments. Moreover, records generated by one department, for example the Publicity Department, may be subsequently used for a variety of different purposes by other departments or by individual employees. The present system is therefore, a particular solution to the problem of classification, although its principles may be more generally applied to other types of business archives.

The construction of the number preceding each catalogue entry is shown in the following example:

Name of Archive	Depositor Indicator	Record Class	Subdivision	Item Number
TR	RAN	AC	I	/I
(Trade Records)	(Ransomes, Sims & Jefferies Ltd.)	(Accounts)	(Ledgers)	

Both the record classes, which are arranged in alphabetical order of class mark, and the class subdivisions, are specified in the contents lists to the catalogue. Further breakdown, by point of origin or by record type, was often necessary, but this did not affect the continuity of the item numbers which run consecutively. Therefore, most class subdivisions are also prefaced by their own contents lists.

Styles of the Firm

The firm adopted various styles while in business at Ipswich. The following list indicates their dates of adoption and the abbreviations used in the catalogue:

1789	RR	Robert Ransome
1809	RSn	Ransome & Son
1818	RSs	Ransome & Sons
1825	JRR	J. & R. Ransome
1830	JRAR	J. R. & A. Ransome
1846	RM	Ransomes & May
1852	RS	Ransomes & Sims
1869	RSH	Ransomes, Sims & Head
1881	RHJ	Ransomes, Head & Jefferies
1884	RSJ	Ransomes, Sims & Jefferies Ltd. (1884 Private Limited Company) (1911 Public Limited Company)

Prior to 1789 Robert Ransome was in business at Norwich trading under the following styles:

1774	Robert Ransome
1784	Ransome & Co.

SUMMARY CATALOGUE

CONTENTS

SUMMARY CATALOGUE

AC   ACCOUNTS

1	Ledgers
5	Cost Accounts
6	Other Accounts
7	Financial Statements
8	Branch Accounts
9	Invoices and Accounting Papers

AC1/   LEDGERS

1–5	Private Ledgers RSJ
6	Memoranda Account Book
7	Nominal Ledger

1–5   PRIVATE LEDGERS RSJ 1884–1944.   Principal real and personal accounts.

6   MEMORANDA ACCOUNT BOOK 1895–1925.   Accounts supplementary to the private ledgers, with composite yearly entries.

7   NOMINAL LEDGER 1920–1939.   Accounts of income and expenditure for ploughs and implements on loan for ploughing matches.

AC5/   COST ACCOUNTS

1–5	Analysis Books of Cost Accounts
6	Details of Cost Accounting System
7–9	Salaries and Wages Accounts
	7 Wages Analyses
	8 Salaries Book—Clerks
	9 Salaries and Wages Book—Staff

1–5   ANALYSIS BOOKS OF COST ACCOUNTS 1885 & 1936–1939.   Annual summary accounts of wages, materials, stores and manufactured goods, excluding general trade expenses. Intended to show profit or loss in individual departments and on different products.

6   FOLDER OF PAPERS 1856–1878.   Notes on the origin and working of the Orwell Works cost accounts system, with details of compilation of stock ledger by product, annual analysis book of cost accounts and component cost accounts. Compiled by R. C. Ransome.

7   WAGES ANALYSIS SHEETS 1871–1939.   Yearly sheets with monthly figures, subdivided into departments and types of work, excluding sundry foremen and staff.

8   SALARIES BOOK 1887–1907.   Clerks. Yearly sections with quarterly figures, subdivided into departments and individual employees. Also list of terminating dates of employment agreements.

9   SALARIES AND WAGES BOOK 1926–1940.   Staff. Yearly sections divided into different departments and staff (salaried, wage earning, Ipswich and Bury warehouse staff). Also Grantham salaried staff 1930–1937 and directors' salaries 1930-1939.

AC6/   OTHER ACCOUNTS

1	Early Accounts
2	Great Yarmouth Accounts
3	Summary RSJ Accounts

1   GENERAL ACCOUNT BOOK RR, RSn, RSs, JRR, JRAR 1804–1839. In two parts, certain accounts in part 2 relating to James Ransome's foundry business at Great Yarmouth. Accounts of income and expenditure 1804–1805; memoranda 1809–1812; stock accounts 1809–1832; statement of profits 1816–1817; account of bad debts and credits 1809–1815; gas works account 1817; account of work which arose primarily from the employment of William Cubbitt 1812–1816; table of profits to determine partners' shares in the business 1824–1839; account of division of profits 1830–1832; annual totals of income 1804–1821; account of quarterly journeys 1809–1815; account of monthly income 1809–1821. The Yarmouth accounts are of monthly income 1805–1809.

2   ACCOUNT BOOK 1805–1807. James Ransome's foundry business at Great Yarmouth.

3   NOTEBOOK 1884–1901. Yearly summaries of principal RSJ accounts and share capital. Credit and debit to income and expenditure; credit and debit to balance sheet; credit and debit to profit and loss account; analysis of value of output; analysis of value of stock; analysis of value of purchases; details of debentures, borrowed capital, shareholdings and Ransome family holdings. Probably private notebook of J. E. Ransome.

AC7/   FINANCIAL STATEMENTS

1–2   FILES OF SUMMARY BALANCE SHEETS JRAR, RM 1837–1850. Includes details of share out of profits amongst the partners. 1837 (30 Jun) for 24 months; 1839 (31 Dec) for 18 months; 1841 (31 Dec) for 24 months; annual thereafter as at 31 Dec.

3   ANNUAL FINANCIAL STATEMENT JRAR 1845. Balance sheet; profit and loss account; trading account.

4   SUMMARY OF ANNUAL FINANCIAL STATEMENTS RM 1846–1848.

5–6   ANNUAL FINANCIAL STATEMENTS RM 1846 & 1848. Balance sheet; profit and loss account; trading account.

7–8   ANNUAL BALANCE SHEETS RM 1849 & 1850.

9   VOLUME OF ANNUAL FINANCIAL STATEMENTS RM, RS, RSH 1851–1880. 1852 and 1853 are combined. Balance sheet; profit and loss account; trading account.

10   VOLUME OF ANNUAL FINANCIAL STATEMENTS RHJ 1881–1883. Balance sheet; profit and loss account; trading account.

11–40 ANNUAL FINANCIAL STATEMENTS RSJ 1941–1971. Audited and printed statements for distribution to RSJ shareholders, with directors' reports, chairman's comments, seven and eight year reviews and general data. Also annual branch balance sheets for Ransomes Sociedad de Responsabilidad Limitada, Buenos Aires 1948–1956.

41–46 FINANCIAL STATEMENTS RSJ 1966–1971. Half yearly summary statements as at 30 Jun.

AC8/   BRANCH ACCOUNTS

1–4   Princes St. Warehouse, Ipswich
5   Odessa Branch

1–2   GENERAL LEDGERS 1916–1947. Princes St. warehouse, Ipswich. Yearly entries after annual stocktaking.

3–4   PRINCIPAL JOURNALS 1902–1928. Princes St. warehouse, Ipswich. Also cash book account for initial work on Nacton site 1946–1948.

5   VOLUME OF FINANCIAL STATEMENTS 1892–1919. Odessa branch. Volume 2. Annual statements are at 31 Oct. Trade account; balance sheet; value of goods sent; cash received and balance due on goods account (monthly); proportions for freight, expenses, debts, profit or loss and capital. Volume 1 is not extant.

AC9/   INVOICES AND ACCOUNTING PAPERS

1–5   MISCELLANEOUS INVOICES 1834–1854. For plough parts, wagon boxes, chaff cutter, iron pot and thrashing machine spares.

6   LIST 1920 (23 Aug). Outstanding debts to RSJ, consequent to the First World War. Arranged by country (Austria, Bulgaria, Germany, Roumania, Russia, Turkey) and subdivided into debtors.

AD   ADMINISTRATIVE AND COMMERCIAL RECORDS

  1   Minutes and Proceedings of Board Meetings
  2   General Administrative and Commercial Records
  3   Labour Records
  4   Premises Records
  5   Materials Records
  6   Branch Records
  7   Commercial Records
  8   General Correspondence
  9   Minor Administrative Records

AD1/   MINUTES AND PROCEEDINGS OF BOARD MEETINGS

  1   Minute Book
  2–10   Reports of Proceedings

1   DIRECTORS' MINUTE BOOK 1884–1937. Number 1. A formal record of resolutions at board meetings, including summary details of the full proceedings. Also subject index.

2–10   REPORTS OF PROCEEDINGS OF DIRECTORS' MEETINGS 1919–1939. Monthly reports divided into the following principal sections, financial/statistical report; list of customers' order in hand including number and value; export trade report; home trade report; factory report; details of capital expenditure and accounts; secretary's report and additions. *Confidential records, special permission required for access.*

AD2/   GENERAL ADMINISTRATIVE AND COMMERCIAL RECORDS

1   NOTEBOOK 1884–1901. Yearly summaries of sales, output and wages statistics. Home sales 1884–1901; export sales 1884–1901; export sales (Europe, Asia, Africa, America, Australasia) 1891–1901; home output 1884–1901; export output 1884–1901; wages divided into departments and types of work 1884–1901; wages divided into day work rates and piece work rates 1884–1901; tonnage input 1884–1899. Probably private notebook of J. E. Ransome.

2   NOTEBOOK 1881–1930. Engineering department. Includes a wide variety of information concerning staff, wages, technical matters, personalities and the First World War. Also subject index. Probably compiled by C. J. Palmer.

3   NOTEBOOK 1833–1881. Ploughs and fittings. Includes a wide variety of information concerning types, production, sales, output, trade mark infringements, prizes, labour and legal actions. Probably notebook of R. C. Ransome.

4   NOTEBOOK 1920–1950. Includes a wide variety of information concerning staff, insurance rates, labour, wages, wartime production, patent agreements and lien.

5   BUNDLE OF PAPERS 1940–1944. RSJ and the Second World War. Mainly correspondence with government departments.

6   FILE 1966. Two RSJ applications for the Queen's award to industry.

1   LIST OF WORKMEN 1835 (23 Oct). In the employ of JRAR. Arranged in order of commencement of employment 1793–1835. Includes notes on abilities, performance, wage rates and personalia. Also contents list and index. Compiled by James Ransome.

2   LIST OF WORKMEN 1843. Employed in the upper foundry of JRAR. Arranged by occupation. Includes individual wage rates and composite wage and employee totals. Compiled by James Ransome.

3   LIST OF WORKMEN 1851. In the employ of RM. Arranged in alphabetical order of workmen, with sub-headings for general occupations. Includes date of arrival, age, wage rate, name and precise occupation.

4–9   REGISTERS OF WORKMEN 1859–1922. Number 1 1859–1872 is divided into four books, each further divided into three sections and each section divided into different occupations. Includes name, date of entering employment, date of leaving employment, cause of discharge, wage rate, manager's initials and subsequent wage increases, each with manager's initials. Number 2 1872–1887 is divided into two books prior to 1881, after which entries are arranged under occupation only. Numbers 3–6 1887–1922 are arranged in alphabetical sections, according to employee's surname. From 1909 (Oct) onwards the employee's age is given. Also list of park department workmen and combined list of agricultural department and machine shop workmen, both in 1875.

10   LIST OF WORKMEN c. 1870. Arranged in alphabetical order. Includes wage rate and initials of respective foreman. Compiled by R. C. Ransome.

11   VOLUME OF NOTES 1887–1924. Typescript notes of events affecting the wages and cost department, especially labour relations and trade unionism. In three sections, general events 1887–1924; labour problems including strikes and disputes 1914–1923; trade unionism. Subject index per section. Compiled by R. B. Reeve.

12–14   APPRENTICESHIP INDENTURES. Ironfounder 1822 (6 Mar); fitter and turner 1854 (28 Sep); ironfounder and engineer 1856 (13 Sep).

15   REGISTER OF APPRENTICESHIP INDENTURES 1838–1872. Divided into apprentices and master apprentices. Includes name, age, art, date of commencing agreement, term of years, date of expiry, wage rates and remarks. Also table comparing wages of "lads" in works with those in offices 1881; regulations for rate of apprenticeship wages by age 1843; regulations over employment of apprentices including wage rates as at

1857 (Feb) and 1861 (Feb). Also the following loose papers, account of monthly salaries 1883; account of weekly apprentices' wages 1883; account of monthly salaries 1884; account of clerks' salaries 1867, 1877 and 1884–1885; two personal files and correspondence.

16   EMPLOYMENT CONTRACT 1900 (9 Jul).   Foreman of lawn mower works.

17   EMPLOYMENT CONTRACT *c.* 1920's.   Blank specimen. Salaried employees.

18–21   CORRESPONDENCE 1901–1904.   Between J. E. Ransome and J. H. W. Pawlyn concerning the latter's employment and the running of the accounts department.

22   RELIEF FUND BOOK 1817–1836.   For the benefit of workmen employed in Ransomes' foundry. List of members of the fund with weekly contribution rate 1834; rules of the fund 1817 with subsequent alterations; account of weekly payments into fund 1817–1824; annual balance sheets 1817–1836; annual reports 1817–1819. Also loose associated papers.

23   RELIEF SOCIETY RULES 1839.   For the benefit of the workmen in the employ of JRAR, replacing above relief fund.

24   FRIENDLY SOCIETY RULES 1842.   For affording relief to workmen in the employ of JRAR, replacing above relief society.

25   INVALIDS BOOK 1838–1849.   Arranged chronologically. Includes wage rate, name, employment, date of leaving work, ailment, medical attention, means of support, remarks and date returned to work.

26   STAFF PENSION FUND REGULATIONS 1949.

27   RULE BOOK *c.* 1850.   Regulations and forfeits to be observed by workmen in the engine room of the Orwell Works. Attached are similar rules for workmen in the smiths' shop, foundry and upper foundry.

28   MEMORANDUM 1959 (28 May).   From L. W. Bryant concerning special training of personnel with comments on selection procedure.

29   ALBUM OF MATERIAL 1851–1852.   Concerns the formation of the Amalgamated Society of Engineers, Machinists, Millwrights, Smiths and Pattern-Makers and its interest in piece work and overtime.

30   NOTES 1915 (13 Sep).   Concerns the applications of the Workers Union and National Union of Gas Workers and General Labourers to the Ipswich and District Engineering Employers Association. Brief notes on Ipswich engineering firms and the labour market.

31   LETTER 1840 (31 Oct).   To the workmen in their employ from JRAR concerning the matter of bribery in the forthcoming municipal election at Ipswich.

32–43   LETTERS, CIRCULARS, NOTICES AND MEMORANDA 1840–1965.   Concerns mainly labour and conditions of employment. Includes two circular letters about the depression of 1921, short-time working and the closure of three principal departments.

44–52   STANDARD INSTRUCTIONS 1969.   Senior appointments and staff changes.

53   PETITION 1857.   From six master apprentices requesting that they be allowed to continue to enter by the gate on the quay.

AD4/   PREMISES RECORDS

      1   Maps
      2–4   Details and Particulars
      5–7   Other Records

1   VOLUME OF MAPS 1846–1847. Orwell Works. Seven maps including ground plans, upper floor plan, tower warehouse plans, general foundry plan and plan of adjacent property. Also two loose general plans 1850 and 1860.

2   DETAILS 1847–1848. Workmen's hall. Contains its history and mode of construction. Its principal purpose was the provision of food and drink.

3   PARTICULARS 1852 (May). Orwell Works land, buildings and plant.

4   DETAILS AND PARTICULARS 1916–1918. Aircraft works. Includes details of shops, plant and staff.

5   NOTEBOOK 1870–1891. Alterations, improvements and repairs to Orwell Works premises. Compiled by H. A. Byng.

6   REPORT 1918 (12 Apr). Concerns the future of the lawn mower works.

7   FAULT BOOK 1963. PAX, PA and intercom.

AD5/   MATERIALS RECORDS

       1–3   Output
       4   Stores
       5   Oil Fuel Supplies and Issues
       6   Government Contract Work
       7–8   Termination of Production

1–2   ANALYSIS BOOKS 1866–1882. Number of goods dispatched from the Orwell Works. Monthly figures with yearly totals for all products and major components.

3   NOTEBOOK 1861–1891. Goods dispatched from the Orwell Works. Monthly figures with yearly totals. Weight of goods sent home and export by steamship 1874–1889; weight of goods sent export 1873–1891; weight of goods sent home 1875–1891; number of goods trucks loaded at the Orwell Works 1874–1890; number of goods trucks loaded at Ipswich Station with steam engines, thrashing machines and straw elevators 1874–1887; number of letters received 1861–1891.

4   NOTEBOOK 1867–1891. Stores. Part 1 concerns purchases and dispatches. Yearly value of invoice purchases 1870–1890; yearly numbers of invoices 1867–1890; yearly numbers of orders including export 1867–1890; yearly value of Great Eastern Railway account charges 1870–1890; yearly value of goods dispatched home and export 1872–1890; average monthly price of warrants 1871–1891; yearly amounts of timber orders 1872–1885; accounts of timber purchases 1879–1883. Part 2 concerns staff details. Notes on arrival and departure 1873–1884; number of staff 1874–1890; notes on wages 1874–1889; list of piece work rates for quay porters 1885.

5   OIL FUEL BOOK 1926–1931. Supplies and internal weekly issues.

6   FILE 1939–1943. Lists of materials supplied on government contracts during the Second World War. Divided into Admiralty, Ministry of Aircraft Production and Ministry of Supply.

7   FILE 1955. Details of termination of wooden thrashing machine production and the transfer of certain lines to Garvie & Sons, Aberdeen.

8   FILE 1955. Details of termination of steam engine parts production, including transfer of certain lines to Robey & Co. Ltd., Lincoln and destruction of patterns as from 1956.

AD6/ BRANCH RECORDS

Town Warehouse, Ipswich and Bury St. Edmunds

1   BOOK OF REGULATIONS 1892. Ipswich town warehouse, RSJ's retail and wholesale outlet for Suffolk. The Bury St. Edmunds warehouse was subsequently included in these regulations as a sub-department. The rules were for the warehouse manager's private reference. Also loose memoranda.

2–4   AUCTION RECORDS 1957. Concerns the stock of both the Ipswich and Bury warehouses and also the Bury premises. Includes two auction catalogues and an account with the auctioneers.

AD7/ COMMERCIAL RECORDS

1–11   REPORTS 1942–1948. General commercial situation and its relationship to RSJ's business. Subjects include prospects for post-war trade especially in agricultural machinery; problems due to the dearth of raw materials; deficit between outstanding orders and current production and potential part for RSJ in European relief programme. Mostly compiled by F. E. Waterman.

12–14   ORDER BOOKS 1938–1943. Numbers 3, 4 and 6. Machinery and components related to wartime production, including government contracts. Order details include customer, address, order number, date, items required, delivery note and cost. Also customer index per book. Book number 3 has loose papers including lists of government orders in hand 1938–1940.

15   ANALYSIS OF EXPORT ORDERS 1934–1943. Portable steam engines and traction engines. Annual totals divided into countries.

E

16   ANALYSIS OF ORDERS 1933–1939.   Lawn mowers. Annual totals, divided into machinery types and sizes.

17   FOLDER OF SALES ANALYSES 1871–1939.   Annual sheets (though variable financial year) with monthly returns, divided into home and export, classes of product and customers goods and bought goods. Figures are gross 1871–1884; gross and net 1885–1892; net 1893–1939.

18–27   EXPORT SALES ANALYSES 1913, 1923–1931, 1933–1934 & 1938–1944.   Annual analyses (though variable financial year), divided into countries and classes of product. Goods sent on consignment are in red.

28–29   EXPORT SALES ANALYSES 1923–1934 & 1937–1941.   Lawn mowers. Annual analyses (though variable financial year). 1923–1924 are divided into monthly returns and 1937–1941 into countries.

30   SALES ANALYSES 1953–1956.   Tractors and implements. Annual analyses with monthly returns for home and export. Also value of orders received, dispatches and unexecuted orders 1953–1956.

31–32   VOLUMES OF HOME PRICE LISTS 1862–1882 & 1896–1902.   General product range. Includes Ransomes' publications as illustrative matter. Also subject index 1896–1902. Office compilations.

33   FOLDER OF DATA 1866–1927.   Price fluctuations. 8 HP portable steam engine and A54 thrashing machine 1866–1927; EC, ECD and "Key Conqueror" export ploughs 1914–1924. Compiled by C. J. Palmer.

34   VOLUME OF PRICE LISTS 1869.   General product range. Includes RSH publications.

35–40   VOLUMES OF PRICE LISTS 1848–1898.   Ploughs and implements. Includes Ransomes' publications. Both office and personal compilations.

41–42   VOLUMES OF PRICE LISTS 1882 & 1884.   Engineering department products. Includes RHJ and RSJ publications.

43–44   VOLUMES OF PRICE LISTS 1920's.   Lawn mower parts. Includes RSJ publications.

45   GENERAL RULES 1921 (May).   For guidance in fixing prices for extras and wearing parts of steam engines, corn mills, electric vehicles and trucks, thrashing machines, ploughs, implements and lawn mowers.

46   MEMORANDUM 1931 (20 Apr).   Concerns prices of parts for export ploughs and implements with statement of profits on cost to be made per part type.

47   EXPORT BOOK 1875–1889.   Peru and United States of Colombia. Ransomes had no agency in either country, their business being transacted mainly through importing houses. The Peru section includes yearly value of sales returns, direct and indirect 1875–1889; list of importing houses; totals of goods sent divided into products 1875–1883; order details arranged by importer 1875–1883. The Colombia section includes yearly value of sales returns, direct and indirect 1875–1883; details of shipping arrangements; list of London importing houses to Colombia not on Ransomes' books; totals of goods sent divided into products 1875–1883; order details arranged by importer 1875–1883. Also loose copy correspondence concerning a Peruvian representative for RSJ 1890; correspondence concerning a Peruvian agency 1907; list of steam engines and thrashing machines sent to Colombia 1897–1921.

48   EXPORT BOOK 1866–1885.   Roumania. Arranged by agencies. Includes historical notes, details of agency agreements and yearly value of sales returns. Agencies are Bucharest, Galatz and Jassey.

49   EXPORT BOOK 1861–1885.   Russia. Arranged by agencies, excluding branches. Includes historical notes, details of agency agreements, yearly value of sales returns and totals

of goods sent, divided into products. Agencies are Charkow, Beltz, Tanganrog, Samara, Saratov, St. Petersburg and Riga.

50–57   IMPLEMENT AGENCIES BOOKS 1914–1950. England and Wales. Lists of agents in alphabetical order of location, including various addenda. North 1916–1930; south and east 1915–1931; Wales, west Midlands and south west 1914–1931; north 1929–1947; south 1931–1950; east 1931–1947; south west 1931–1949; Wales and west Midlands 1930–1949.

58–59   IMPLEMENT AGENCIES BOOKS 1917–1946. Scotland. Arranged as above.

60   IMPLEMENT AGENCIES BOOK 1930–1948. Ireland (Ulster and Eire). Arranged as above.

61   NOTEBOOK 1804. Business journey by James Ransome to northern England and the west Midlands. Includes copy correspondence and personal travelling account.

62   LETTER 1839 (11 May). Robert Ransome to J. A. Ransome concerning the latter's recent business journey to plough agents in England.

63   VOLUME OF COPY CORRESPONDENCE 1875–1876. James Drey Gay to R. C. Ransome, concerning market potential for RSH goods in India and Ceylon. Includes reference to RSH competitors.

64   NOTES ON TRAVELLING 1897. Made by J. E. Ransome for E. C. Ransome. Incorporates both general and specific advice on personal promotion techniques.

65   FILE OF CORRESPONDENCE AND REPORTS 1928–1929. Relates to the business of F. Walker, an RSJ sales representative in southern England.

66   REPORT 1929. Visit by A. Rackham to twenty-one firms in the USA. A detailed and comprehensive comparative survey of plant, premises, production techniques, labour relations and conditions of employment. The report is followed by a comparison of the operating costs of electric and gasoline tractors in John Deere plough works shop 1925–1926.

67   REPORT 1930. Visit by V. W. Bone to the USA. Mainly concerned with explanatory talks with the Case Company over co-operation in export sales.

68   ITINERARY 1961. Tour by K. M. Hicks to South and Central America.

69–80   MISCELLANEOUS COMMERCIAL RECORDS 1845–1969. Home customers. H. N. Silwell, Dunchurch 1845; Edmund Barham, Westfield 1854; William Russell, London 1854; H. Pattison & Co., Stanmore 1927–1928; J. Morrissey & Sons, Nenagh 1928; Air Ministry Works Services 1932; Anglo-Iranian Oil Co. Ltd., England. Also circular letters to RSJ home dealers 1962–1969.

81–90   MISCELLANEOUS COMMERCIAL RECORDS 1906–1961. Foreign customers. Includes Vaccaro & Cie, Philippopolis 1906; Jessop & Co. Ltd., Calcutta 1924; Mangold Bros., South Africa 1937–1938; Turkish Government 1943; Pashabhal Patel & Co., Bombay 1943; Indian Government 1944; Case Co., Racine 1945; United Africa Co. Ltd. and Ford Motor Co. Ltd., 1947; Agricultural Engineers Association Ltd. 1959–1961.

AD8/   GENERAL CORRESPONDENCE

1–21   POSTALLY USED ENVELOPES AND ENTIRE LETTERS 1842–1851. Apparently retained primarily for philatelic interest, but containing useful information about Ransomes' sales techniques and the state of the implement trade in the 1840's.

22   LETTER BOOK 1875–1955. "Curious Letters". A compilation of various dates and items in no apparent order, mainly of a humorous nature.

AD9/ MINOR ADMINISTRATIVE RECORDS

1–6   INTERNAL WORKS FORMS 1880–1900. Specimens and samples. Includes engine shop, lawn mower works, turnery, turnery stores and yard traction crane forms.

CO   LEGAL RECORDS OF COMPANIES AND BUSINESSES

1   Records of Partnerships, including Capital
2   Records of Registered Companies, including Capital
3   External Agreements
4   Real Estate Records
5   Patenting Records
6   Trade Mark Records

CO1/   RECORDS OF PARTNERSHIPS INCLUDING CAPITAL

1–17   Partnership Records
     1   RSn
     2   RM
     3   RS
     4–17   RSH
18–19   Capital Records

1   DEED OF CO-PARTNERSHIP 1809 (1 Dec). Party 1: Robert Ransome of Ipswich, ironfounder; Party 2: James Ransome of Ipswich, ironfounder and son of Party 1. Establishing the firm RSn as a seven year partnership with a capital of £3,776, joint ownership of patents and equal division of profits.

2   DEED OF DISSOLUTION OF PARTNERSHIP 1852 (15 Jun). Party 1: Robert Ransome, James Allen Ransome and William Dillwyn Sims of Ipswich, ironfounders; Party 2: Stafford Allen of Church Street, Stoke Newington, Middlesex; Party 3: Charles May of Ipswich, ironfounder. Dissolving the partnership of Parties 1 and 3, styled RM, as from 1851 (31 Dec), with the retirement of Party 3 and with the consent of Party 2. The partnership now to comprise Party 1 only, styled RS.

3   PARTNERSHIP BOOK 1863–1865. Includes copy and original material concerning the admission of John Head to the partnership of RS. Correspondence, notes of discussion and of partners' capital, draft and copy of final articles of agreement 1863 (30 Dec) and minutes of partners' meetings in respect of the articles 1864 (Jan–Nov).

4   ARTICLES OF PARTNERSHIP 1869 (1 Jan). Draft. Parties: James Allen Ransome, William Dillwyn Sims, Robert Charles Ransome and James Edward Ransome. Establishing the firm RSH as a twelve year partnership, with proportional division of profits and losses and joint ownership of patents.

5–6   PROVISIONAL AGREEMENT 1869 (1 Jan). Original and draft. Party 1: James Allen Ransome, William Dillwyn Sims, Robert Charles Ransome and James Edward Ransome; Party 2: John Robert Jefferies. To admit Party 2 to the partnership of Party 1, styled RSH, two and a half years after its commencement on 1869 (1 Jan). Provisions for Party 2's salary and eventual share in the partnership.

7–15   SECONDARY AGREEMENTS 1869–1875. Subsequent to CO1/4. Concerns provisions for decease of any partner in respect of allocating annual profits.

16–17   ARTICLES OF AGREEMENT 1875 (20 Jul). Original and draft. Party 1: Robert Charles Ransome; Party 2: John Head; Party 3: James Edward Ransome; Party 4: John

Robert Jefferies. To continue the partnership of RSH for the remainder of the term of twelve years, with the omission of James Allen Ransome, died 1875 (29 Apr) and with re-apportionment of profits.

18   LETTER 1838 (11 Oct). To Dykes Alexander from James Ransome, on behalf of JRAR, acknowledging short term loan of £2,000.

19   CAPITAL LEDGER 1865–1883. Accounts of capital investments in RS, RSH and RHJ, from the admission of John Head to the partnership of RS until the formation of RSJ as a private limited liability company. Also lists of capital creditors and payments, cash creditors, bonds and securities.

CO2/   RECORDS OF REGISTERED COMPANIES, INCLUDING CAPITAL

    1–10   RSJ
            1–5   Memorandum and Articles of Association
            6–10   Stocks and Shares
    11   Ruston & Hornsby Ltd.
    12   D. Lorant Ltd.
    13–23   Société Balkanique Commercialle & Industrielle

1   COMPANY BOOK RSJ 1884–1909. Company records relative to RSJ as a private limited liability company. Includes Articles of Association 1884 (1 May); related registration documents and subsequent legal advices.

2   COMPANY BOOK RSJ 1911–1937. Company records relative to RSJ as a public limited liability company. Includes Memorandum and Articles of Association 1911 (30 May); related registration documents and subsequent alterations to the articles.

3–5   CIRCULAR LETTERS 1949 & 1968. To RSJ shareholders concerning Articles of Association and annual general meeting.

6   STOCK TRANSFER REGISTER 1911–1948. RSJ $4\frac{1}{2}\%$ first mortgage debenture stock.

7   PROSPECTUS 1911 (18 Apr). For the issue by RSJ of 133,334 $5\frac{1}{2}\%$ cumulative preference shares at £1 each and £166,667 $4\frac{1}{2}\%$ first mortgage debenture stock at $99\frac{1}{2}\%$. Includes details of profits 1901–1910.

8   TRUST DEED 1911. Blank specimen. In the name of RSJ constituting and securing $4\frac{1}{2}\%$ first morgage debenture stock.

9   CIRCULAR LETTER 1922 (11 Mar). To RSJ shareholders concerning non-payment of half-yearly dividend on $5\frac{1}{2}\%$ cumulative shares due to the continued trade depression.

10   FILE OF SPECIMEN DOCUMENTS 1948–1949. Concerns issue by RSJ of £800,000 $3\frac{3}{4}\%$ first mortgage debenture stock in place of above $4\frac{1}{2}\%$ stock.

11   MEMORANDUM AND ARTICLES OF ASSOCIATION 1918–1919. For Ruston & Hornsby Ltd. as a limited liability company.

12   BOOK OF SHARE CERTIFICATES 1939–1951. D. Lorant Ltd.

13–23   COMPANY RECORDS AND CORRESPONDENCE 1911–1923. Société Balkanique Commercialle & Industrielle. Includes Articles of Association 1911 (29 Aug); annual reports 1914, 1920, 1922 and correspondence. RSJ had a share-holding interest in the company.

CO3/   EXTERNAL AGREEMENTS

1   GUARANTEE 1927 (28 Dec). By RSJ to The Royal Bank of Scotland for £1,500 on account of the Maston Engineering Co., Ladylands, Corstophine, Edinburgh, at 5% interest per annum.

CO4/   REAL ESTATE RECORDS

1   CONVEYANCE 1852 (15 Jun). Party 1: Robert Ransome and James Allen Ransome of Ipswich, ironfounders and Stafford Allen of Church Street, Stoke Newington, Middlesex, manufacturing chemist; Party 2: Charles May of Ipswich, ironfounder; Party 3: William Dillwyn Sims of Ipswich, ironfounder; Party 4: George Josselyn of Ipswich, agent. Concerns certain of the freehold property, part of the assets of the late partnership of RM, Parties 1 and 2, on the occasion of the retirement of Party 2 and the formation of the partnership of RS, Parties 1 and 3.

CO5/   PATENTING RECORDS

      1–5   Ploughs
      6–8   Lawn Mowers
      9–12   Inkstands
      13   General

1   PATENT SPECIFICATION 1785 (1 Apr). Transcript. (UK.) For tempering plough-shares. In the name of Robert Ransome.

2   PETITION 1803 (31 Aug). Transcript. To George III from Robert Ransome of Ipswich, seeking a grant of letters patent for his method of making and tempering cast iron ploughshares.

3   PATENT SPECIFICATION 1808 (30 May). Enrolment duplicate. (UK.) For improvements on the wheel and swing plough. In the name of Robert Ransome of Ipswich.

4   PATENT SPECIFICATION 1810 (6 Jun). Draft. (UK.) For improvements in the body of the wheel and swing plough. In the name of Robert Ransome of Kelvedon, Essex.

5   MEMORANDUM OF AGREEMENT 1853 (1 Dec). Between RS (plaintiffs) and William Busby, Newton-le-Willows, Bedale (defendant) concerning the latter's infringement of RS plough patents.

6   LEGAL ADVICE 1895 (17 May). From William Tarpmael, patent agent, concerning whether an intended patent for lawnmowers would infringe patent number 15636 UK, granted to James Shanks 1893.

7   PATENT SPECIFICATION 1902 (29 Mar). Copy of provisional. Number 7540 UK. For improvements in land rollers and mowing machines. In the name of James Edward Ransome of Holme Wood, Ipswich.

8   REPORT AND CORRESPONDENCE 1931. Extracts. Concerns Curle's improvements to the bearings for the front roller of lawn mowers and their patentability with reference to RSJ.

9–11 PATENT SPECIFICATION 1861 (16 Oct). Enrolment duplicate and printed. Number 933 UK. For improvements in inkstands. In the name of Robert Ransome. Also enrolment duplicate of specification drawings.

12   ARTICLES OF AGREEMENT 1875 (3 Nov). Party 1: Robert Charles Ransome and James Edward Ransome of Ipswich; Party 2: Thomas de la Rue & Co. of 110 Burnhill Row, London, merchants and manufacturing stationers. Concerns sale and manufacture of inkstands by both parties as under above patent. Also historical note on their manufacture.

13   LEGAL ADVICE 1839 (Nov). From J. Campbell, attorney general and John Pontifix, to R. G. Ransome concerning the rights of masters and workmen in inventing, developing and patenting unspecified machinery.

CO6/ TRADE MARK RECORDS

      1   Registration
      2–8   Litigation

1   VOLUME OF REGISTERED TRADE MARKS 1877–1930. Agricultural and horticultural machinery, namely Class 7, under the Trade Marks Registration Act, 1875. A compilation of cuttings from the official printed trade mark lists.

2   VOLUME OF LITIGATION 1872–1882. For the following cases:
      i   1872–1874. Plaintiffs, James Allen Ransome, William Dillwyn Sims, Robert Charles Ransome, John Head and James Edward Ransome. Defendant, John Cooke. Concerns the defendant's manufacture and sale of ploughshares of the size, weight and markings used by the plaintiffs. Chancery number 160 1872.
      ii   1881–1882. Plaintiffs, Robert Charles Ransome, John Head, James Edward Ransome and John Robert Jefferies; Defendants, John Graham and Richard Crush Joslin. Concerns RHJ registered trade marks numbers 12373–12375 and the Trade Marks Registration Act 1875. High Court of Justice, Chancery Division number 2049, 1880 and Supreme Court of Judicature, Court of Appeal.

3–7   VOLUMES OF LITIGATION, NOTES AND CORRESPONDENCE 1881–1882. Relative to above case CO6/2 (ii).

8   LIST OF ENGLISH PLOUGH FOUNDERS 1882–1883. Relative to above case CO6/2 (ii). Compiled to indicate whether the founder had ever pirated Ransomes' trade marks or not.

DO DRAWING RECORDS

      1   Drawings
      2   Registers and Indexes

DO1/   DRAWINGS

Wherever possible Ransomes' own drawing number has been retained as part of the catalogue number to facilitate reference. The material at Reading is as follows:
Originals, tracings and prints—card catalogue
Spasmodic survival apart from virtually complete standard list series—DO1/L. Series represented are:

no   Drawings entered in five drawing ledgers DO2/1–5. Pre DO1/9899 are mid and
prefix late nineteenth century drawings of general product range. DO1/9990 ff. are mainly steam engineering drawings *c.* 1880–1940's.

D   Drawings entered in four design drawings registers DO2/9–12.

L   Drawings entered in standard list drawings register DO2/14. Standard steam engineering components.

SK   Drawing office sketch books DO1/SK2/74 = drawing office sketch book number 2 drawing number 74.

RSJ   Drawings entered in thrashing machinery department drawings registers (not extant)— "RSJ" prefix series.

E   Drawings entered in engineering department drawings registers (not extant)—"E" prefix series.

LM	Drawings entered in lawn mower works drawings registers (not extant)—unprefixed series.
LS	Drawings entered in lawn mower works drawings registers (not extant)—"LS" prefix series.
(LM)	Unnumbered drawings of machinery manufactured by the lawn mower works.
MD	Drawings of machinery and components manufactured by RSJ for the Ministry of Defence 1938–1945—"MD" prefix series.
RH	Drawings or copies thereof of Ruston & Hornsby Ltd., Ruston Proctor & Co. Ltd. and Ruston Proctor & Co. drawings. Accumulated at the time of RSJ's merger with Rustons.
(RH)	Unnumbered tracings by RSJ of Ruston & Hornsby Ltd. drawings.
N	*Barcograph transparencies* (6·5 × 4·75 inches, negative and positive). Barcograph transparencies of drawings were first made as a security precaution during the Second World War and the practice continued thereafter. The drawings copied go back to the 1880's in places and for the great majority the transparencies are the only record now extant. Negatives are of RSJ drawings, positives are of Ruston & Hornsby Ltd. drawings. The transparencies are numbered N1 onwards in order of copying. The catalogue information is to be entered in the drawings card catalogue and will include the transparency number, though filed according to the drawing number concerned. The Reading holding as at 1974 (Jul) is *c.* 15,000 transparencies of all engineering department and thrashing machinery department product drawings pre N40,000. The transparency numbers are also entered in certain of the drawings ledgers and registers.

DO2/ REGISTERS AND INDEXES

1–8	Ledger Drawings	
	1–5	Ledgers
	6–8	Indexes—Engineering Department Products
9–12	Design Drawings Registers	
13	Ledger and Design Drawings Index—Engineering Department Products	
14–15	Standard List Drawings	
	14	Register
	15	Index
16–17	Registers of Customers	

1–5   DRAWINGS LEDGERS 1834–1951. Ledger numbers 0–11000. Ledgers 1 and 2 are the first drawing ledgers of the firm, covering the general range of products. Numbers were assigned according to sectional subject heads and drawings subsequent to the original number are designated by an alphabetical suffix. Format per entry is number, size, date of office drawing, date of shop drawing, description and remarks. Ledgers 3 and 4 are principally concerned with steam engineering. Each drawing number has a page headed by the machinery type, with the subsidiary letter suffixed numbers added below and individually registered as the main numbers in ledgers 1 and 2. Barcograph transparency numbers are also indicated where applicable. Ledger 5 contains overspill entries from ledgers 1–4.

6–8   DRAWINGS INDEXES 1857–1929. Ledger series. Engineering department products divided into twelve sections, section eleven being absent. Each section is in alphabetical order of parts and components, with divisions for engine HP or mill size. References include ledger drawing number with size/type abbreviation and date. Sections 1–9, portable, stationary and vertical steam engines, pumping engines and corn mills 1857–1899; section 10, "New Design" portable steam engines 1883–1929; section 12, traction engines and road locomotives 1877–1913.

9–12 DESIGN DRAWINGS REGISTERS 1887–1950. Design numbers 501–23226. Format per entry is number, date, description, drawing source, whom drawing sent to or received from and number and type of copies sent. Size and type of design drawing are also given from D3380 onwards.

13 DRAWINGS INDEX. Ledger and design series. Engineering department products. Arranged by product types in alphabetical order, according to the schedule at the front of the volume. Also a few entries for agricultural machinery and lawn mowers. References comprise description, drawing number, type and often customer.

14 STANDARD LIST DRAWINGS REGISTER 1885–1942. Standard list numbers 1–2137. Divided into two sections. Format per entry is number, whether obsolete, description, drawing office date, date of issue, number of copies issued, supersedes, superseded by and date superseded. Barcograph transparency numbers are added in red above the standard list numbers.

15 DRAWINGS INDEX. Standard list series. Arranged by alphabetical subject sections and in rough numerical order per section. Format per entry is number, description and whether obsolete. Index is a copy of the original destroyed 1917 (Apr) with additions thereafter.

16–17 REGISTERS OF CUSTOMERS 1911–1948. Drawing office. Drawing dispatches and receipts. Drawings mainly supplied as blueprints by RSJ and occasionally drawings remitted by customers to RSJ. In alphabetical order of customers, including internal departments of RSJ. Individual customer entries in order of dispatch or receipt. Format per entry for dispatch is number of blueprints sent, blueprint number, drawing number copied from, description and dispatch date. Format per entry for receipt is number and type of drawing received, drawing number, description and receipt date.

ET TECHNICAL RECORDS—Experimental and reference

1   Records of Experiments and Trials
2   Technical Reference Records—Ransomes Products
3   Technical Reference Records—General

ET1/ RECORDS OF EXPERIMENTS AND TRIALS

1–3   Steam Engineering
4–10   Ploughs and Implements
       4–9   JRAR and RSJ
       10   J. & F. Howard

1 EXPERIMENTS BOOK 1846–1889. Steam engines, railway materials and thrashing machines. Fifty-nine sets of experiments/trials.

2 EXPERIMENTS BOOK 1884–1886. Steam and gas engines. Seven sets of experiments/ trials.

3 FILE 1902–1904. Experimental military hauling engines manufactured by RSJ for the War Office. Includes summary of trials, technical notes, correspondence and a photograph.

4 DETAILS 1838 (12 Nov). Plough trials at the premises of Thomas Fox.

5   BUNDLE 1839–1840. Concerns trials of Kent ploughs. Mainly correspondence between JRAR on one part and either Thomas Bentley, John Oakley or Addis Jackson on the other.

6   NOTES *c.* 1840's. Trials of Suffolk, Rutland, Bedfordshire and Lincolnshire ploughs. Includes sketches.

7   PLOUGH REGISTER 1888–1889. Ploughs remitted to RSJ from various makers as samples or for inspection. The last ten entries are experimental ploughs manufactured by RSJ.

8   REPORT 1944 (22 Sep). Field test of four-furrow "Supertrac" PE 760 plough.

9   REPORT 1963 (1 Apr). Ploughing competition to determine the desirability of introducing a plough body which would do whole work for the BPA competition.

10   FOLDER OF PHOTOGRAPHS 1905–1915. Experimental agricultural implements tested and mainly manufactured by J. & F. Howard, Bedford. Comprises 252 prints affixed to captioned foolscap sheets.

ET2/   TECHNICAL REFERENCE RECORDS—Ransomes Products

        1–11   Compilations of General Reference
             3–5   Ploughs and Implements
             6–10   Steam Engineering
             11   Tea Machinery
        12–20   Compilations for Personal Reference
             12   Engineer's Notebook
             13–20   Annotated Publicity

1   PUBLICITY ALBUM 1901–1907. General products. Publicity arranged by rough subject divisions with various memoranda and notes.

2   VOLUME OF PUBLICITY AND NOTES 1867. General range of products.

3   DRAWINGS ALBUM *c.* 1840's. Plough types. Fifty drawings nearly all water colours. Compiled by J. E. Ransome.

4   DRAWINGS ALBUM *c.* 1840's. Agricultural implements and other products. Fifty drawings nearly all water colours. Compiled by J. E. Ransome.

5   DRAWINGS AND ENGRAVINGS ALBUM *c.* 1840's. JRAR agricultural implements. Includes a few non-agricultural items.

6   VOLUME OF DRAWINGS 1870's. RSH steam engines, steam thrashing machines and corn mills. Sixteen coloured drawings on linen mounted tracing paper.

7   BOOKLET 1877 (Jan). John Head, "A Few Notes on the Portable Steam Engine, with an Account of its Construction and General Adaptation". First edition. Concerns RSH products.

8   VOLUME OF PUBLICATIONS 1877–1878. Different language versions and editions of above booklet. English, French, Spanish and German. Compiled by C. J. Palmer.

9   BOOKLET 1877 (Jun). Second English edition of the above. Three copies, one with technical annotations.

10   BOOKLET 1877 (Jun). Second edition, German version of the above.

11   PUBLICITY COMPILATION 1888 & 1901–1906. RSJ tea machinery. Includes various technical annotations.

12   ENGINEER'S NOTEBOOK 1888–1908. William Fletcher. Fletcher's notes on steam engineering cease *c.* 1890 and thereafter the book was used to record details of steel traction gearing.

46

13   VOLUME OF PUBLICITY AND NOTES 1881–1883. J. A. Harvey. Seven annotated RHJ publications followed by notes, principally on steam engineering.

14   VOLUME OF PUBLICITY AND NOTES 1869 & 1874–1875. John Head. Seven RSH publications followed by notes on steam engineering and thrashing machinery.

15   PUBLICITY COMPILATION 1889 & 1900–1933. W. N. King. Nine annotated RSJ publications and one Ruston & Hornsby Ltd. publication.

16   PUBLICITY COMPILATION 1900–1927. W. N. King. Six annotated RSJ publications, one Haighs (Oldham) Ltd. publication and one Herbert Morris Ltd. publication.

17   PUBLICITY COMPILATION 1901 & 1909. W. N. King. Two annotated RSJ publications.

18   PUBLICITY COMPILATION 1886. C. J. Palmer. PN 1980E RSJ. Includes additional notes.

19   PUBLICITY COMPILATION 1857 & 1859. Thomas Parkes. Includes catalogue for John Fowler Jnr.

20   PUBLICITY COMPILATION 1901 & 1905. W. G. Scott. Two annotated RSJ publications.

ET3/   TECHNICAL REFERENCE RECORDS—General

1   BOOK OF GEOMETRICAL DEFINITIONS *c.* 1850. R. C. Ransome.

2   VOLUME OF TECHNICAL PUBLICATIONS 1865–1877. J. E. Ransome and John Head.
i   J. E. Ransome, "Ploughs and Ploughing" 1865
ii   J. E. Ransome, "Double Furrow Ploughs" 1872
iii   John Head, "On the Rise and Progress of Steam Locomotion on Common Roads" 1873
iv   John Head, "On the Combustion of Refuse Vegetable Substances" 1877
v   John Head, "A Few Notes on the Portable Steam Engine, with an Account of its Construction and General Adaptation" 1877

3–8   PRESS CUTTINGS ALBUMS 1881–1910. "Engineering Papers". Extracts from general engineering papers not kept in RSJ's works library. Divided into subject sub-sections. Originally four volumes, volumes 1–3 being in 2 parts each. Volume 3, part 1 is absent.

9   LITERARY MANUSCRIPT 1840's. W. L. Rham, "Essay on Agricultural Mechanics". Apparently a copy of the original with comments, possibly by J. A. Ransome. Includes sketches. There is no indication that the essay was ever published.

10   BOOKLET 1854. "De L'Agriculture en Quinconce au Moyen d'un nouveau systeme d'instruments", second instalment. Concerns scarifiers and dibblers. In French with manuscript English translation affixed.

11   CUTTINGS ALBUM 1862–1877. Ploughs. Includes twenty-four manufacturers' publicity and press advertisements. Contents captioned and arranged spasmodically under manufacturer. Compiled by J. E. Ransome.

12–17   VOLUMES OF PRINTED PATENT SPECIFICATION DRAWINGS 1786–1871. Reapers and mowers. Probably acquired by RSJ during their administration of the former Hornsby premises at Grantham, whilst in merger with Ruston & Hornsby Ltd. The texts of the printed specifications are not included. Comprises 350 patents, all UK.

18   PRESS CUTTINGS ALBUM 1869–1872. Reapers and mowers. Concerns twenty-six manufacturers.

19   TWO DIAGRAMS 1848 (Sep). Two coloured, mounted, linen engravings of a stationary steam engine and a steam locomotive.

20–22   PRESS CUTTINGS ALBUMS 1861–1871. Steam ploughing and cultivating machinery. Concerns various systems and their manufacturers.

23   SET OF SEVEN PHOTOGRAPHS *c.* 1872–1878. J. Fowler & Co., Leeds. Concerns the Sutherland reclamations, probably at Strath Tirry. Fowler PhN W159–165.

24   PHOTOGRAPH ALBUM 1860's & 1870's. Traction engines, ploughing engines, road rollers, road locomotives, steam omnibuses and road and farm steamers. Thirty-nine captioned prints relating to eleven manufacturers.

25   PRESS CUTTINGS ALBUM 1871–1872. Traction engines, road locomotives, road steamers, farm steamers and road rollers. Concerns six manufacturers and includes technical notes. Compiled by John Head.

26   PATENT SPECIFICATIONS ABSTRACTS 1855–1877. Gas engines. Fifty-eight patents, all UK. Includes sketches.

27   LIST OF PATENT SPECIFICATIONS 1830–1893. Lawn mowers. Comprises 180 entries all UK.

28   PATENT SPECIFICATIONS ABSTRACTS 1830–1864 & 1876–1877. Lawn mowers. Thirty patents, all in above list.

29   NOTES 1883. Lawn mower patents, all UK.

30   PATENT SPECIFICATION 1881 (3 Jun). Number 16175 Germany. For lawn mowers. In the name of J. A. St. Biernatzki, Hamburg.

31   PATENT SPECIFICATION 1920 (21 Dec). Number 14077/20. Australia. For an electric power attachment for lawn mowers. In the name of Edward Bistee Keele, Lockleys, South Australia.

32   CUTTINGS ALBUM 1877–1911. Lawn mowers. Includes manufacturers' publicity and press extracts with 101 manufacturers represented, several being US firms. Also machine and manufacturer index 1886–1888. Compiled by J. E. Ransome.

33   PATENT SPECIFICATION 1914 (9 Apr). Number 27842 amended UK. For apparatus for drying tea, coffee, grain or other substances. In the name of Samuel Davison, Belfast.

34   PATENT SPECIFICATION 1915 (21 Oct). Number 289 UK. For tea leaf rolling machinery. In the name of Samuel Davison, Belfast.

MP   MANUFACTURING AND PRODUCTION RECORDS

1   Registers and Lists of Production
2   Manufacturing Working Papers
3   Parts, Repairs and Outworks Records

1–2   ENGINE REGISTERS *c.* 1846–1880. Series 1. In order of engine numbers 1–4299. Precursors of MP1/7–19. Register number 1, engine numbers 1–2237 *c.* 1846–1872 includes engine number, description, date and customer. Register number 2, engine numbers 2238–4299 1871–1880 includes engine number, particulars, order number, order date, dispatch date and customer. Superseded after engine number 2757 by MP1/7 below. Entries still continued to be made here, though in a very brief manner after number 3640. Notes and technical memoranda affixed to end papers.

3–5   ENGINE REGISTERS 1870–1874. Series 2. In order of engine numbers 1626–3060. More abbreviated entries than MP1/1–2 with different dates. Probably of completion of manufacture. No customer details. Includes engine number, manufacture-date, engine type and remarks. Precursors of MP1/20–32.

6   LIST OF RM STEAM ENGINES *c.* 1846–1851. Engine numbers 1–46. Includes number, description, cost price, selling price, where sent and how employed. Compiled by R. C. Ransome.

7–19   ENGINE REGISTERS 1877–1945. Sales number series 2758–44141. A continuation of the previous series of engine numbers. In order of engine numbers, assigned in order of sale. Includes sales number, boiler number, customer, stock number and remarks. The final register 1928–1945 has some numbers, especially the later ones with "5" prefixes. It also contains engine sales numbers 8400–84030, 1930's for portable and semi-portable steam engines built by Robey & Co. Ltd. for RSJ. Those where the initial "8" is replaced by "6" were built for Ruston & Hornsby Ltd. by Robeys.

20–32   ENGINE REGISTERS 1877–1942. Boiler number series 1–11200, A201–P 649. In order of boiler numbers, stamped one per boiler, in order of completion of manufacture. Includes boiler number, sales number, engine type and class, engine details, boiler details and remarks. By an order of 1902 (1 Oct) boiler numbers, old series, ceased at 11200. Thereafter the initial "11" was replaced by "A" commencing therefore at A201 and continuing to A999. After this a "B" series was started at B000, "B" replacing "12". This continued on through the alphabet to P649. "I" was not used.

33   SUMMARY TRACTION ENGINE REGISTERS 1864–1942. Sales numbers 1000–44114. The registers, no longer extant, were presumably an amplification of the traction engine entries in the two above series of general engine registers. Includes number, date, customer and engine type.

34–39   CUSTOMER INDEXES. Traction engine registers. These are the original indexes, one per register. Includes customer, address and register page number.

40–41　REGISTER NOTES 1891–1907.　Traction engine registers. Sales numbers 8704–11483 and 14327–20046. In rough chronological order. Each engine has a numbered folio headed by engine HP and type, including boiler number, sales number, dispatch date, customer, address and a detailed technical specification, with drawing numbers and references to the turnery books (MP2/2–26) wherever appropriate. Both have contents lists. Volume 2 also has a customer index. Volume 1 compiled by W. Fletcher.

42　LIST OF RSJ STEAM WAGONS 1920–1930.　In chronological order. Includes date, sales number, boiler number, customer, turnery books reference, order number, wagon type and remarks.

43　STEAM WAGON AND OIL ENGINE REGISTER 1921–1927.　Export machines. Divided into $3\frac{1}{2}/4$ BHP "Wizard" oil engines; 6/7 BHP "Wizard" oil engines and steam wagons. In approximate order of dispatch date. Includes customer, order book folio, sales number, dispatch date and description.

44　CUSTOMER INDEX.　Corn mill register. The actual register is no longer extant. Includes customer, address and register page number.

45–49　CUSTOMER INDEXES.　Thrashing machine registers. The registers are no longer extant. One index per register. Includes customer, address and register page number.

50　REGISTER OF PLOUGH TYPES 1839–1943.　In alphabetical sections according to plough marks with chronological entries per section. Includes mark, name, date of first manufacture, whom made for and description. Entries prior to 1901 (May) were transferred from older registers if the entries were still extant then. New entries added thereafter up to 1943.

51　REGISTER OF PLOUGH TYPES 1882–1915.　In order of initial dispatch dates. One plough mark per page, including whom made for, date of initial dispatch, detailed technical description and illustrative photograph. Three contents lists.

52　LIST OF RSJ MANUFACTURING MARKS 1940's.　Ploughs and implements. Marks C, D, M, PD, RP, S, TD and TS series. Includes description and selling name.

53　LIST OF RSJ TROLLEY BUSES 1925–1948.　Arranged by customers' orders. Includes customer, number of buses supplied, date and detailed technical information.

54　LIST OF RSJ TROLLEY BUSES 1926–1941.　Export machines. Arranged by customers' orders. Includes customer, date and very detailed technical information.

MP2/　MANUFACTURING WORKING PAPERS—Engineering Department

1–27　Turnery Books
　　1　　Standard Details
　　2–27　Orders
28–30　Boiler Shop Books
　　28　　Standard Details
　　29　　Orders
　　30　　Specifications
31–32　Special Requirement Books
33–34　Engine Registration Books
35–37　Engine Testing Records
　　35–36　Log Books
　　37　　Test Report
38–193　Report Books
　　38–184　Engines
　　185–193　Corn Mills
194–202　Dispatch Books

I   TURNERY BOOK 1891–1907. Standard details. Turnery copies of standard details sheets for steam engines and boilers (originals were kept in the drawing office). The sheets are headed by engine or boiler type and date with standard details following, including drawing numbers. Also index of engine and boiler types.

2–26   TURNERY BOOKS 1860–1949. Orders. Twenty-five books containing forty-seven volumes of turnery notes. The notes comprise turnery copies of order details for engineering department products, as different from standard details (originals were kept in the drawing office). The sheets are headed by title of work, customer, order number and date, with order details below, including drawing numbers. Also composite index per book of customers and products.

27   TURNERY BOOK 1917 (3 Aug–28 Nov). List of orders. In chronological order. Includes order number, customer, date and order details.

28   BOILER SHOP BOOK 1896–1944. Standard details. Boiler shop copies of standard details sheets for boiler plates (originals were kept in the drawing office). The sheets are headed by engine or boiler type, date and drawing number, with standard details below. Some orders are also included. Index of boiler and engine types.

29   BOILER SHOP BOOK 1895–1946. Orders. Boiler shop copies of details of orders for boiler plates as different from standard details (originals were kept in the drawing office). The sheets are headed by engine or boiler type, customer, order number and date with order details below. Combined machinery and customer index.

30   BOILER SHOP BOOK c. 1905. Specifications and standard requirements. Arranged in sections according to boiler or engine type, each section being divided into individual entries for different plate types. Compiled c. 1905 with notes and alterations added thereafter.

31–32   SPECIAL REQUIREMENTS BOOK 1909–1932. Number 6 and number 8 only. The engineering department compiled such a book periodically to indicate individual customer and foreign law requirements for specific machinery details.

33–34   ENGINE REGISTRATION BOOKS 1898–1914. Sales numbers 12235–16010 and 25001–30091. A draft means of correlating engine sales numbers with engine boiler numbers. The volumes are in order of sales numbers and include boiler number, HP, customer and stock number.

35–36   LOG BOOKS 1896–1916. Manufacturing tests on high speed stationary steam engines. In chronological order of tests. Includes date, customer, engine size, engine sales number and detailed technical information.

37   TEST REPORT 1919 (3 Jul). Steam engine number 767. Built by E. R. & F. Turner, Ipswich.

38–184 ENGINE REPORT BOOKS 1874–1910. The reports were made per customer order by the engine erecting department after manufacture and testing were complete and prior to dispatch. They contain technical details of the various component engine and boiler parts including sketches, as they were arranged for packing, sometimes indicating packing costs. The reports are headed by order number, engine sales number, engine boiler number from 1878 onwards, customer, report date, whom erected by and HP, followed by the report. The only extant access to the reports is via the engine registers, sales numbers series, which give the report date per entry. MP2/42–48 also include corn mill reports.

185–193 CORN MILL REPORT BOOKS 1881–1910. Compiled as engine report books. The reports are headed by order number, mill number, customer, report date and customer's order number. Reports prior to 1881 are included in the engine report books MP2/42–48. Mill numbers are given from 1890 (Aug) onwards, 1222–1810 but very spasmodically before, the mill size usually being entered instead. In the absence of the corn mill register, the reports are the principal manufacturing records extant.

194–202 DISPATCH BOOKS 1883–1932. Engineering department products, divided into engines, boilers and corn mills. Individual product entries, including customer, product type and HP, register number (sales and boiler for engines) and dispatch date. There are weekly totals for the number of engines, boilers and corn mills dispatched with returns and yearly net summaries minus returns.

MP3/ PARTS, REPAIRS AND OUTWORKS RECORDS

1	Pattern Book
2–13	Engineering Department
	2—5 Vertical Oil Engines
	6–9 Portable, Stationary and Vertical Steam Engines
	10–11 Steam Wagons
	12–13 Traction Engine Gearing
14–17	Plough Works

1 PATTERN BOOK 1849–1888. Pattern marks A1–1000 B1–999 C1–359. Assigned chronologically. Includes customer where applicable. Wide product range, including steam engineering, thrashing machinery, barn machinery, railway work, works fittings and equipment and numerous sundries.

2–4 PARTS REGISTERS 1923–1925. Vertical oil engines. Each contains parts list for standard engines; parts alterations list; list of engines with parts varying from the standard; list of engines rebuilt with additional or altered parts. Includes drawing numbers.

5 STANDING ORDERS 1920's. Men sent out to outworks, repairs and alterations jobs on vertical oil engines.

6–7 PARTS LIST 1929 (Dec). Compound portable steam engine, Dutch law requirements. Part numbers 1–228 with parts photographs.

8 LIST 1920's. Steam engine wheel sizes.

9 FILE 1946 (18 Jul–14 Dec). Portable, stationary and vertical steam engine parts for African customers.

10–11 PARTS LISTS 1925 (Mar). "Ransome" steam wagon. Part numbers SW301–734.

12 TRACTION GEARING REGISTER c. 1920–1948. Traction engines, road locomotives, ploughing engines, steam tractors and oil tractors. Sectional arrangement according to engine type and HP. Includes standard list drawing number, gearing description, pattern mark, ledger drawing number, old design number and remarks. Notes of pattern destruction are in red. Also lists of pattern marks, gearing weights and steel castings.

13 TRACTION GEARING SUPPLY BOOK 1924–1937. For spare parts and outworks. Traction engines, ploughing engines, steam wagons and steam tractors. In order of supply. Includes dispatch date, quantity, description, pattern mark, stock details and remarks.

14 PARTS REGISTER 1870–1955. Ploughs and implements. Plough parts divided into breasts, slades, shares and sundries, each arranged by plough marks. Implements divided into potato diggers, mealie planters, swath turners, root or turnip thinners, cultivators and potato planters, each arranged by implement marks. The register was begun in 1870, but in 1901 most extant entries for plough parts were transferred to new registers MP3/15–17. Entries however continued to be made for implements and a few specific plough types. Notes of obsolescence and destruction of patterns are in

red and were added up to 1955, after which the plough works were moved to a new site at Nacton.

15   PARTS REGISTER 1840–1955. Plough shares. Arranged both in order of marks and of part numbers. The register was begun in 1901 with the transfer of extant entries from earlier registers, including MP3/14 and continued up to 1955, prior to the move to Nacton. Notes of obsolescence and destruction of patterns are in red.

16   PARTS REGISTER 1844–1954. Plough breasts, slades and wheels, horse rakes and haymakers. The plough parts sections are arranged by marks or part numbers, the implement sections by machinery types. The register was begun in 1901, with the transfer of extant entries from earlier registers, including MP3/14 and continued up to 1954, prior to the move to Nacton. Notes of obsolescence and destruction of patterns are in red.

17   PARTS REGISTER 1842–1956. Plough sundries. Divided into types of sundries; sundries for specific plough and part types; plough castings; miscellaneous castings. The register was begun in 1901 with the transfer of extant entries from earlier registers, including MP3/14 and continued up to 1956 when the plough works was moved to Nacton. Notes of obsolescence and destruction of patterns are in red.

P   PUBLICATIONS, PROMOTIONS AND ADVERTISING RECORDS

1   General Compilations of Publications
2   Individual Advertising and Servicing Publications
3   Posters and Display Matter
4   House Journals
5   News Releases
7   Records of Advertising Campaigns and Events
8   Printing Proofs and Artworks
9   Registers and Indexes

PI/A   GENERAL COMPILATIONS OF PUBLICATIONS—Ransomes, including
                                                     Branches and Subsidiaries

1–2   Early Albums *c.* 1800–1845
3–57   Principal Reference Set 1852–1939
58–85   Personal Reference Sets and Compilations
      58   J. Adams
      59–60   J. A. Harvey
      61   J. R. Jefferies
      62–72   C. J. Palmer
          62–69   Export
          70–71   Home
          72   RS Catalogues
      73   Robert Ransome
      74–85   J. H. Rogers
86–122   Subsidiary Reference Sets and Compilations
      86–87   RSH Compilations
      88–89   RHJ Compilations
      90–94   RSJ Compilations
      95–97   1876–1881 Publications
      98–101   Instruction Booklets
      102–122   Others
123–124   Catchpole Engineering Co. Ltd. (RSJ Subsidiary)

1–2   PUBLICITY ALBUMS RR, RSn, RSs, JRR, JRAR *c.* 1800–1845.   Comprising 200 publications affixed to two guard albums.

3–57   VOLUMES OF GENERAL PUBLICATIONS RS, RSH, RHJ, RSJ 1852–1939.   Principal series PN1–13586. Most volumes include a few unnumbered items and occasionally reprints of earlier servicing literature. There are also occasional absentees from the numerical sequence per volume. The following years are absent, 1863–1867, 1873–1878, 1880, 1882, 1883, 1890, 1895, 1896, 1899, 1900, 1911–1913, 1915 and 1923.

58   VOLUME OF PUBLICATIONS RSJ 1891 & 1894–1896.   J. Adams. Fourteen publications.

59–60   VOLUMES OF EXPORT PUBLICATIONS RSH 1872–1879.   J. A. Harvey. Thirty-eight publications.

61   VOLUME OF PRICE LISTS RSH 1871–1880.   J. R. Jefferies. Fifty-nine publications divided into home and export.

62–69   VOLUMES OF EXPORT PUBLICATIONS RSH, RHJ, RSJ 1873–1891.   C. J. Palmer. Originally nine volumes, volume 1 being absent. Comprising 196 publications.

70–71   VOLUMES OF HOME PUBLICATIONS RSH, RHJ 1869–1885.   C. J. Palmer. Fifty-one publications.

72   VOLUME OF CATALOGUES RS 1862–1863 & 1867.   C. J. Palmer. Seven catalogues.

73   VOLUME OF PUBLICATIONS JRAR 1844.   Robert Ransome. Three publications.

74–84   VOLUMES OF PUBLICATIONS RS, RSH, RHJ, RSJ 1862–1885.   J. J. Rogers. Comprises 381 publications.

85   VOLUME OF PUBLICATIONS RS 1857–1862.   J. J. Rogers. Divided into four parts, fifty publications.

86–87   VOLUMES OF PUBLICATIONS RSH 1869–1876.   One volume is home the other export, fifty-five publications. RSH compilation.

88–89   VOLUMES OF CATALOGUES RS, RSH, RHJ 1868–1882.   One volume is home the other export. Catalogues with home price lists, fifty-nine publications. RHJ compilation.

90–94   VOLUMES OF CATALOGUES RS, RSH, RHJ 1862–1883.   Seventy-three publications. RSJ compilation.

95–97   VOLUMES OF PUBLICATIONS RSH 1876–1881.   Seventy-eight publications.

98–99   VOLUMES OF INSTRUCTION BOOKLETS RS, RSH, RHJ 1868–1882.   Twenty-nine booklets.

100–101   VOLUMES OF INSTRUCTION BOOKLETS RS, RSH 1868–1869.   Two copies of four-language compilations.

102   VOLUME OF PUBLICATIONS JRAR 1844.   Eighteen publications.

103   VOLUME OF PUBLICATIONS RS 1857.   Ten publications.

104   VOLUME OF PUBLICATIONS AND NOTES 1856–1857.   Various. Four RS publications, one Samuel Worssman & Co., one R. H. Bushe, the RASE implement catalogue for the Chelmsford show 1856 (15–18 Jul) and three manuscript RS items.

105   VOLUME OF CATALOGUES 1857–1858.   Eighteen publications, also four JRAR publications *c.* 1830.

106   VOLUME OF CATALOGUES RS 1857–1862.   Seven publications.

107   VOLUME OF CATALOGUES RS 1862–1867.   Twenty-one publications divided into English, special and foreign.

108   VOLUME OF CATALOGUES RS 1863–1867.   Seven publications.

109   VOLUME OF CATALOGUES RS, RSH 1867–1870.   Thirteen publications.

110   VOLUME OF CATALOGUES RS, RSH 1867–1870.   Nine publications.

111   VOLUME OF CATALOGUES RSH 1876–1878.   Eight publications.

112   CATALOGUE AND PRICE LIST RS 1867 (May).   Special bound version of PN500 and 498 for the Paris Universal Exhibition.

113   CATALOGUE AND PRICE LIST RSH 1879 (Apr).   Special bound version of PN1320E and 1421E.

114   CATALOGUE AND PRICE LIST RHJ 1882 (Jan).   Special bound version of PN1550E.

115   CATALOGUE AND PRICE LIST RSJ 1884 (Oct).   Special bound version of PN1850E and 1917H.

116   CATALOGUE AND PRICE LIST RSJ 1886 (Jan).   Special bound version of PN1980E.

117   CATALOGUE AND PRICE LIST RSJ 1886 (Jan).   Special bound version of PN2020E.

118   CATALOGUE AND PRICE LIST RSJ 1886 (Jul).   Special bound version of PN2020E for the visit to the Orwell Works of the Colonial and Indian Exhibition (23 Jul). Includes a guide to the works.

119   CATALOGUE AND PRICE LIST 1871 (Jan).   Special bound version of PN800.

120   VOLUME OF CATALOGUES RS 1860 (Jul & Dec).   Two publications.

121   VOLUME OF PUBLICATIONS RSH, RSJ 1883 & 1914.   Two publications.

122   VOLUME OF PUBLICATIONS RSJ 1912 & 1922.   Three publications.

123–124 FOLDERS OF PUBLICATIONS 1948–1968.   Catchpole Engineering Co. Ltd. an RSJ subsidiary.

P1/B   GENERAL COMPILATIONS OF PUBLICATIONS—Various Firms

1–2   Great Exhibition, London 1851
    1   Agricultural Implement Exhibitors
    2   General Exhibitors
3   James & Frederick Howard, Bedford 1856–1862
4   RASE Show, Warwick 1859
5   Foreign Language Publications 1858–1869

1   VOLUME OF PUBLICATIONS 1851.   Thirty-nine publications of agricultural implement exhibitors at the Great Exhibition. Originally forty publications, that for Mary Wedlake & Co. being lost. Includes Fowler & Fry; James & Frederick Howard; William Crosskill; RM; William Smith; J. C. Grant; Smith & Co.; Clayton Shuttleworth & Co.; Barrett, Exall & Andrewes; R. Hornsby & Son; John James & Co.; John Thompson; Whitmee & Chapman; Winton & Sons; Shand & Mason; Sholl; Cooch; John Pannell; John Whitehead; Ransome & Parsons; W. Hensman & Son; Tuxford & Sons; McCartney & Drummond; Robert Maynard; Edward Hill & Co.; Edward Packard.

2   VOLUME OF PUBLICATIONS 1851.   General exhibitors at the Great Exhibition. Comprises 134 publications.

3   VOLUME OF PUBLICATIONS 1856–1862.   James & Frederick Howard, Bedford. Sixteen publications.

4   VOLUME OF PUBLICATIONS 1859.   Twenty publications of agricultural implement exhibitors at the RASE show, Warwick (12–15 Jul). Originally volume 6 of a set of six volumes of 129 exhibitors' publications, volumes 1–5 now being lost. Volume 6 originally contained twenty-two publications numbers 108–129, letters S-W, but numbers 109 and 128 are also lost. Includes William Snowden; William Smith; N. Smith; Charles Thomas; W. Tasker & Sons; E. R. & F. Turner; Robert Tinkler;

Tuxford & Sons; John Tye; W. S. Underhill; T. Wheeler; William Waller; Wallis & Haslam; Samuel Worssam & Co.; J. Warren; John Whitehead & Son; F. P. Walker & Co.; Edward Weir; Williamson Brothers.

5   VOLUME OF PUBLICATIONS 1858–1869. Thirty-one foreign language publications of which twenty-seven are either foreign manufacturers' publications or English manufacturers' publications in foreign languages, two are agents' catalogues and two are general technical booklets. Includes A. Huet; Coleman & Morton; Richmond & Chandler; C. N. Racotta; The Reading Iron Works Ltd.; Gehr, Kappe & Co.; Enklaar,Riphagen & Cie; H. Cegielslei; Collins & Co.; S. Worrsam & Co.; Strobl & Baris; Hayes & Son; Walter A. Wood; H. Tilkin-Mention & Co.; Samain; Theophil Weiss; Carl Lachermaier; H. F. Eckert; Stefan Vidats; F. Kugler; G. Sigl; Erzherzogl; John Tye; Picksley, Sims & Co.; E. & T. Fairbanks & Co.; Robey & Co.

P2/A   INDIVIDUAL ADVERTISING AND SERVICING PUBLICATIONS—Ransomes

PN1–   Numbered Publications (card catalogue)
1–91   Unnumbered Publications 1820's–1961
      1   JRR
      2–10   JRAR
      11–16   RM
      17–36   RS
      37–46   RSH
      47–91   RSJ

P2/B   INDIVIDUAL ADVERTISING AND SERVICING PUBLICATIONS—Various Firms

1	John Barford 1837
2	E. H. Bentall 1850
3	The British Oil Pump Co. 1920's
4	The British Manzel Oil Pump Co. 1920's
5–6	C. &. W. Chandler Ltd. *c.* 1926
7	Farm & Industrial Implements Co. Inc. late 1920's
8	William Foster & Co. *c.* 1940
9	John Fowler 1862
10	Richard Garrett & Sons Ltd. 1925
11–19	James & Frederick Howard 1851–1916
20–32	James & Frederick Howard Ltd 1917—*c.* 1930
33	James Hunter *c.* 1840
34	International Crushing & Grinding Equipment Ltd. *c.* 1933
35	R. M. Marples & Son Ltd. early 1950's
36	Thomas M'Kenzie & Sons 1868
37	Joseph Mealor 1893
38	Jr Melichar-Umrath *c.* 1936
39	Oliver Chilled Plough Co. 1890
40–41	Frederick Ransome & Co. 1850's
42	S. & E. Ransome & Co. 1858
43	Ransomes & Rapier 1887
44	Rotary Hoes Ltd. 1953
45–49	Ruston & Hornsby Ltd. 1926–1934
50	Samuelson & Co. 1900
51	James Sharp 1773–1777

52	The Shell & BP Farm Service 1961
53	S. A. Buxton, Guilyan & Co. Lda. *c.* 1930
54	South African Farm Implement Manufacturers Ltd. 1950
55	Williams, White & Co. 1895
56	Worthington Mower Co. 1928

P3/ POSTERS AND DISPLAY MATTER

| 1–4 | Poster Albums |
| 5–7 | Display Matter |

1–4   POSTER ALBUMS RHJ, RSJ 1882–1930. Mounted and folded posters accompanied by printing details. In chronological order. Comprises 161 posters.

5–7   DISPLAY MATTER 1870's & 1950's. Two drawings and one illustration.

P4/ HOUSE JOURNALS

1–2	Ransomes Reporter
3–9	Ransomes Lawn Mower Review
10–12	Ransomes Record
13–42	Ransomes Roundabout

1–2   RANSOMES REPORTER 1956. Volume 1, numbers 1 and 2. Quarterly bulletin.

3–9   RANSOMES LAWN MOWER REVIEW 1960–1962. Quarterly bulletin.

10–12   RANSOMES RECORD 1961–1963. Numbers 1–3. For distribution at agricultural shows.

13–42   RANSOMES ROUNDABOUT 1964–1969. Numbers 1–20, 22, 22A and 23–30. Bi-monthly. Number 21 was never produced.

P5/ NEWS RELEASES

| 1–29 | RSJ 1958–1965 |
| 30 | Catchpole Engineering Co. Ltd. 1960–1969 |

P7/ RECORDS OF ADVERTISING CAMPAIGNS AND EVENTS

1–6	General Press Advertising	
	1–3	Agricultural Machinery
	4–6	Lawn and Grass Mowing Machinery
7–10	Special Advertising Events	
	7	Nacton Press Conference 1956
	8	Edinburgh-London Non-Stop Motor Mower Attempt 1959
	9–10	Launch of the "Cavalier" Combine Harvester 1965–1966
11–28	Publicity Remittance	
	11–26	Covering Letters
	27–28	Specimen Remittances

1–3   PUBLICITY PRESS CUTTINGS ALBUMS 1965–1969. Advertisements of dealers and distributors of RSJ agricultural machinery. Three albums, two export, one home.

4–6   PUBLICITY PRESS CUTTINGS ALBUMS 1965–1966. Advertisements of dealers and distributors of RSJ lawn and grass mowing machinery. Three albums, two home, one export.

7   PUBLICITY PRESS CUTTINGS ALBUM 1956. Press conference demonstrating RSJ's new plough works at Nacton, opened 1955. Includes a note on the press response.

8   PUBLICITY PRESS CUTTINGS ALBUM 1959. Edinburgh-London non-stop motor mower attempt. Made by five students of Harfield Technical College, using an RSJ 24 inch "Matador" mower. Includes cuttings, photographs, news releases, correspondence, timetable of journey and list of local papers along the route.

9   FOLDER OF CUTTINGS 1965 (Sep–Nov). Results of publicity and promotion of RSJ high output, twin drum, "Cavalier" combine harvester. Divided into different types of advertising media.

10   FILE OF TESTIMONIALS 1966 (Oct–Dec). Great Britain users of above combine harvester.

11–26   SPECIMEN LETTERS RSH, RSJ 1875–1895. For remittance with publications, soliciting testimonials or notifying dealers and agents.

27–28   SPECIMEN REMITTANCES RSJ 1923–1927.

P8/   PRINTING PROOFS AND ARTWORKS

      1–17   Albums of Printing Block Proofs
           1–8   General Series
           9–10   Ploughs
           11–12   Agricultural Implements
           13–14   Lawn and Grass Machinery
           15   Thrashing Machinery and Combine Harvesters
           16   Sundries
           17   Ruston & Hornsby Ltd., Grantham
      18–19   Individual Printing Block Proofs
      20–22   Administrative Records

1–8   ALBUMS OF PRINTING BLOCK PROOFS c. 1850–1949. General series. A means of reference for the illustration of Ransomes' publications. Arranged in sections according to implement and machinery types, of which there are general contents lists per album, except album 7. There are also individual proof numbers assigned in sections, according to this typological format. The majority of proofs are captioned, some with printing details and costs. Album 1 contains woodcuts, but thereafter the proofs are mainly from half-tone electros or line blocks. Each album has an index of plough marks.

9–10   ALBUMS OF PRINTING BLOCK PROOFS 1950–1969. Ploughs. A continuation from the end of the general series. Each proof is accompanied by a standard printing details sheet. Also detailed contents lists of proof numbers.

11–12   ALBUMS OF PRINTING BLOCK PROOFS 1949–1969. Agricultural implements. Arranged as "Ploughs" above.

13–14   ALBUMS OF PRINTING BLOCK PROOFS 1950–1969. Lawn and grass mowing machinery. Arranged as "Ploughs" above.

15   ALBUM OF PRINTING BLOCK PROOFS 1950–1968. Thrashing machinery and combine harvesters. Arranged as "Ploughs" above. Also forty-eight general composite proofs.

16   ALBUM OF PRINTING BLOCK PROOFS 1949–1968. Sundries. Mainly grain driers, crop sprayers and trailers. Arranged as "Ploughs" above.

17   ALBUM OF PRINTING BLOCK PROOFS c. 1920's–1935. Ruston & Hornsby Ltd., Grantham. Arranged in eight sections by implement and machinery types. Proofs numbered but in no sequence, undated and uncaptioned. General contents list. Sources are half-tone electros and line blocks. Album compiled by RSJ during their administration of the former premises of R. Hornsby & Sons Ltd., Grantham whilst in merger with Ruston & Hornsby Ltd.

18   SET OF PROOFS *c.* 1810–1825. Four different proofs from RSn and RSs woodblocks.

19   PROOF 1871. Electro of "Ravee" double decker road steamer, made by RSH for the Indian Government.

20   ORDER BOOK 1965. Invoices of advance requisitions for artwork, blocks and electros for publicity purposes.

21   ORDER BOOK 1965–1966. Invoices of requisitions for printed matter for publicity purposes.

22   STATEMENT 1898 (30 Nov). To RSJ from Grant & Co. Ltd., London as November account for printing of posters, with details of stock per poster then paid for.

P9/   REGISTERS AND INDEXES

    1–2   Catalogue, Circular and Show card Registers

1–2   CATALOGUE, CIRCULAR AND SHOW CARD REGISTERS 1931–1958. In order of PN 9895–17998. Includes date, amount ordered, description, date of distribution to office, prints, price and remarks.

PH   INTERNAL PHOTOGRAPHIC RECORDS

    2   Compilations of Prints
    3   Individual Prints
    4   Registers and Indexes

PH2/   COMPILATIONS OF PRINTS

    1–27   General Series Albums
    28–34   "In Work" Series Albums
    35–39   Thrashing Machinery Series Albums
    40–48   General Compilations
    49–51   Lawn Mower Compilations
    52–53   Trolley Bus Compilations

1–27   PHOTOGRAPH ALBUMS *c.* 1856–1947. General series. PhN 1–11597. Prints are captioned and there is also a card catalogue. Subject indexes in volumes 1–3 only.

28–34   PHOTOGRAPH ALBUMS 1943–1963. "In Work" series. Compiled according to implement and machinery types, namely, ploughs (two albums); thrashing machines, combine harvesters, balers, crop sprayers and grain driers (two albums); implements and MG crawler tractors (one album); harrows, subsoilers, mole drainers, beet lifters, potato diggers and land levellers (one album); lawn mowers, electric vehicles, sundries and agricultural machinery parts (one album). Prints are not captioned, but assigned numbers with an "R" prefix, in chronological order. Their register PH4/2 is extant.

35–39   PHOTOGRAPH ALBUMS 1931–1960's. Thrashing machinery series. Mainly a compilation of general series prints in order of PhN, but given a further number for this series 1–698, successively assigned. Prints are nearly all uncaptioned. A machinery type index PH4/3 is extant.

40–48   PHOTOGRAPH ALBUMS *c.* 1856–1920. General product compilations. Principally from the general series. *c.* 1,100 prints.

49–51   PHOTOGRAPH ALBUMS 1904–1924. Lawn mowers. Compiled from general series. Ninety-one prints.

52   PHOTOGRAPH ALBUM 1926–1929. Trolley buses. Compiled from general series. Thirty-four uncaptioned prints.

53   PHOTOGRAPH ALBUM c. 1935. Trolley buses in Cape Town. Fifty uncaptioned prints.

PH3/   INDIVIDUAL PRINTS

     PhN1–   General Series—card catalogue
     PhN R1– "In Work" Series

PH4/   REGISTERS AND INDEXES

     1   Index—General Series—Engineering Department Products
     2   Register—"In Work" Series
     3   Index—Thrashing Machinery Series

1   PHOTOGRAPH INDEX. General series. Engineering department products. Originally compiled c. 1930 with additions up to c. PhN 15,000.

2   PHOTOGRAPH REGISTER. "In Work" series PhN R1–2442. Includes date, number, size, description and whom taken by.

3   PHOTOGRAPH INDEX. Thrashing machinery series. Machinery types. Includes new and old PhN.

SH   SHOW AND EXHIBITION RECORDS

     1   Certificates
     2   Registers and Lists of Awards
     3   General Records

SH1/   CERTIFICATES

     1–3   London 1851
     4   Hanover 1852
     5   Paris 1855
     6   Rouen 1856
     7   Amsterdam 1857
     8–9   Zaandam 1859
     10–11   St. Petersburg 1861
     12–13   Haarlem 1861
     14   Hamburg 1863
     15   Constantinople 1863
     16–17   Stettin 1865
     18   Paris 1867
     19   Akola 1868
     20–21   Brussels 1868
     22   Hanover 1869
     23–26   Santiago 1869
     27   Alford 1870
     28   Göteborg 1871
     29   Vienna 1873

30	Bremen 1874
31	Warsaw 1874
32–34	Brussels 1874
35	Stanišlawowie 1875
36–37	Mitau 1875
38–41	Santiago 1875
42	Maggio 1876
43	South Kensington 1876
44	Melle 1877
45	Cape Town 1877
46–50	Paris 1879
51–55	Sydney 1879
56	Békés 1880
57–65	Melbourne 1880–1881
66	Lucknow 1881
67–68	Paris 1881
69	London 1882
70	Severinoflla 1883
71	Trebandrum 1884
72	Calcutta 1884
73–76	London 1885
77	Amsterdam 1886
78–79	Adelaide 1887
80	Newcastle upon Tyne 1887
81	Karkhov 1887
82	Barcelona 1888
83	Melbourne 1889
84	York 1889
85	Kingston 1891
86–90	Launceston 1891–1892
91	Philippopolis 1892
92	London 1892
93–94	Hobart 1894–1895
95	Bucharest 1906
96	Ireland 1907
97	Nagpur 1908
98	London 1909
99	Ekaterinoslav 1910
100	West Siberia 1911
101–104	Caledon 1924
105	Quito 1922
106	London 1924
107	Blackpool 1927
108	Buenos Aires 1931
109	Suffolk 1957–1961

SH2/ REGISTERS AND LISTS OF AWARDS

1   PRIZE REGISTER 1841–1926. Detailed compilation, arranged by implement and machinery types, with miscellaneous loose or affixed related items.

2   PRIZE LIST 1807–1912. Chronological list detailing show or exhibition, nature of award and items of manufacture concerned.

SH3/   GENERAL RECORDS

SP   **SOCIAL AND PERSONAL RECORDS**

SP1/   GENERAL REFERENCE RECORDS

1   FIRM HISTORY 1774–1928. C. J. Palmer, "The History of the Orwell Works". A typescript history with documentary illustration. Complete with complex paginated text, three indexes and special summaries. The text is divided into eleven periods, each designated by a letter A-M (I and J were not used) and each with a contents list and summary. Each period is then individually paginated, prefixed by the period letter. Periods: A 0–14 1774–1830; B 0–6 1830–1840; C 1–38 1840–1850; D 1–66 1850–1860; E 1–80 1860–1870; F 1–83 1870–1880; G 1–124 1880–1890; H 1–42 1890–1899; K 1–168 1900–1914; L 1–120 1914–1918; M 1–338 1918–1928. The indexes are, persons; implements and machinery; general. The full catalogue entry includes contents lists for each period of the text and individual cataloguing treatment for the inserted documentary matter. Compiled by Palmer during 1928–1930, subsequent to his retirement from the firm after 60 years service.

2   FIRM HISTORY 1939–1961. C. W. H. Cullingford, RSJ works historian. Compiled mainly from yearly desk diaries.